Interpersonal Skills

Interpersonal Skills

Bob Wright

SRN, RMN, Hon MSc (Leeds)

Interpersonal Skills
Bob Wright, SRN, RMN, MSc (Leeds)

ISBN: 978-1-905539-37-6

First published 1992
New updated edition 2007

British Library Catalogue in Publication Data
A catalogue record for this book is available from the British Library

Notice
Clinical practice and medical knowledge constantly evolve. Standard safety precautions must be followed, but, as knowledge is broadened by research, changes in practice, treatment and drug therapy may become necessary or appropriate. Readers must check the most current product information provided by the manufacturer of each drug to be administered and verify the dosages and correct administration, as well as contraindications. It is the responsibility of the practitioner, utilising the experience and knowledge of the patient, to determine dosages and the best treatment for each individual patient. Neither the publisher nor the authors assume any liability for any injury and/or damage to persons or property arising from this publication.

The Publisher
To contact M&K Publishing write to:
M&K Update Ltd · The Old Bakery · St. John's Street
Keswick · Cumbria CA12 5AS

Tel: 01768 773030 · Fax: 01768 781099
publishing@mkupdate.co.uk
www.mkupdate.co.uk

Designed & typeset in 11pt Usherwood Book by Mary Blood

Contents

ABOUT THE AUTHOR

Bob Wright SRN RMN HonMSc (Leeds)
Bob Wright was until recently a Clinical Nurse Specialist in crisis intervention in the Accident and Emergency Department at Leeds General Infirmary. He has developed his experience in counseling and as a workshop facilitator over a number of years, in this country as well as in Australia and the USA. He is the author of two other books Caring in Crisis and Sudden Death.

ACKNOWLEDGEMENTS

To the following who contributed and edited the original series:

OPEN LEARNING ADVISOR
Glennis Johnson BSc

EDITORS
Susan Bird BA (Nurs) RGN CCNS CertEd (FE) FRSH
David Rennie DYCS DSW CQSW

Introduction

You may have begun a new career or you may have decided to look again at the way you communicate in your work. Perhaps you are already helping people who are unable to do some things for themselves. Perhaps these people also need a little encouragement or help to decide how best to undertake a task, or even to think about doing it. You may be very familiar with providing this kind of assistance: it may have become second nature to you and require no conscious effort on your part. Over the years, you will have become more and more proficient without even noticing, as everyone does in so many areas of life. At whatever level you work, now or in the future, you have to communicate. Experienced professionals and novice care workers alike need to communicate meaningfully with their clients. To do so successfully you need to understand the skills required and how to practise them.

ACQUIRING SKILLS

Have you ever watched a child thread a needle or hold a pen for the first time? Do you remember his first faltering efforts? You yourself learned in just the same way, but now you would probably get on with it without even thinking.

If you drive, ask yourself when you are next waiting at a red light whether you remember changing down gears, coming to a halt and putting the hand brake on. Think back to those early driving lessons, when you went carefully through every individual stage, acutely aware of each one.

Just as we developed these abilities so we can acquire new skills for our work, and they will become equally familiar to us. The difference is that we are doing things for people – and no two people are alike. You only have to sit in a railway station and observe all the different faces, shapes and sizes, walks and voices to be reminded of this fact.

Performing a task skilfully is not enough; we also need to be able to communicate with the people we are helping. Fortunately, we have all spent our lives developing interpersonal skills and as you begin to study communication you will realise that you already have a great deal of experience on which you can build.

All of us are born with the potential to communicate. As we grew up we developed skills that helped us to understand the rules for living alongside others. For example, we soon learned when to stop and listen to what others have to say and when not to interrupt them.

As babies grow they develop skills in communication. Initially, they scream and demand, and we give food. Eventually, they begin to wait for more appropriate times and to fit in with meal times. As the child grows he becomes more and more responsible, creates bonds that he values, and learns that these bonds can be threatened if he does not learn the rules.

He learns about giving and receiving, about friendships and relationships. He experiences joy and pain and finds ways of communicating these feelings. He learns about things he will eventually take for granted, such as everyday conversation and the skill it requires, because it is not just about words but about the way he looks, his facial expressions and body language. In other words

> *'It's not what you say but the way that you say it'*

USING SKILLS

All of these interpersonal skills, now second nature to you, are used automatically as you attend to the routine, practical needs of your client. But your client may also have many complex needs which are not purely practical, and which he does not even realise himself. He may need help in coping with feelings, handling distress and change, finding words to express himself. He will want to be understood.

Of course, the need to be understood is not exclusive to your client because you too will want to be understood. This need can often give rise to simple expressions of frustration familiar to us all, such as:

> *'She does not understand me'*

If you have ever tried to obtain something from some organisation (something which seems very simple to you and readily available) you will probably have asked:

> *'Do you understand what I am saying?'* or

> *'Is it clear what I want?'*

When progress is not forthcoming you may use sarcasm to make your point, for example:

'Do you understand plain English?' or

'It seems simple enough to me'

At some point most teenagers will complain they are not understood. Elderly people may feel misunderstood, perhaps by a younger person. Children may not respond because they may not understand the words spoken to them. If we ourselves have a problem, we search for someone who understands. You are working through this book because you want to understand or communicate better with others.

You may have to work with people across a wide range of ages and disabilities. Some disabilities will be apparent, others will not. Some clients will express their need for help clearly in plain speech. Others will be unable to speak or will not have the words to do justice to how they feel, and this may result in behaviour that is difficult to understand or tolerate. This behaviour may be the only way that someone has to communicate how they feel.

Some people manage to communicate well. Others, because they are in pain, feel frustrated or sad or disadvantaged, may not communicate well. Some may never have had the words to communicate with, or may not have the words with which you are familiar. Others may not speak the same language as you, or may not have the physical mechanism to talk. For a variety of reasons some people may not have developed skills in this area and may always have simply shouted people down in order to get what they wanted.

However, communication is not simply about words – it also has a physical aspect. The clothes we wear, whether the colours match or not, may cause a communication problem. We may not feel comfortable if someone talks to us from a very close position or we may wonder what their tone of voice means. How we judge appearances and posture will have a profound influence in our encounters with others.

DEVELOPING SKILLS

If we have a better understanding of interpersonal skills we can be more effective personally and particularly in our roles as care workers. In this role we need to develop these skills, noting aspects of our own lives which may affect our progress.

Inside every carer is a person, the individual behind the role. The two sides of the individual are not easily separated because what affects one side affects the other and increased skills in communication will benefit all aspects of our lives.

You bring into your work all the communication skills you learned in your family and the society in which you live. You are a unique individual and so is your client. You have to learn to understand each other before you can work together usefully.

Learning to communicate effectively will involve examining some everyday events in your daily life, but you will not have to set aside a large amount of time for your learning because you can incorporate it into your life, both inside and outside work.

Looking at the skills you already have, and how they can be developed, will be stimulating for your life at home and at work. Communicating, both in short-term and long-term relationships, in our work, play and intimate lives, lies at the heart of our existence as people.

To the reader

Here are some questions which may occur to you before you start to read this book

Who is this book for?

Anyone involved in caring. It has been designed with you – the reader – in mind. We've tried to make it look and feel friendly and attractive.

Do I need to enrol in a course to use this book?

Certainly not, although you may find that it is used by many caring courses. You can use it on your own, at your workplace as part of an assessment programme, if you're in employment, or as part of a more formal training programme at a college or other institution.

Where can I read this book?

Anywhere you like. You can read it in 'snatches', if this is more convenient for you, or you can interrupt your reading to do some of the exercises. It may help you to write on it, if it's your own copy. As you will see, the book has been designed to be used in a very flexible way.

Are there any special features that I should be aware of before starting to read this book?

You'll find it a great help to know the following:

Definitions

Sometimes a key word might be unfamiliar to some readers, or we might want to be sure that the precise meaning is clear. We have tried to pick out such words and give their meaning at the place where the word is first mentioned. The word and its definition have been set off in the margin.

Examples

There's no substitute for a good example to make a point or convey a message. We've included as many examples as possible and have set these off from the main text with boxes, so that you can skip them if you like, or locate them again if you found them particularly helpful.

Exercises

These have been set off from the text in boxes and in a different typeface. The exercises can extend your knowledge considerably and reinforce what you've read in the main text. You can do the exercises on your own, with a group, or under the direction of a tutor. Or you can choose not to do them at all, or to do them later, after you've read and absorbed the text. The choice is yours.

Remember: this is *your* book – enjoy it!

ABOUT TERMINOLOGY

Throughout the text the recipients of all types of care are referred to as 'clients' and those involved in providing the care as 'care workers'. For simplicity, clients are always referred to as 'he' and care workers as 'she'.

1 What are interpersonal skills?

Most of us need to communicate with others from birth. We gain support, comfort and recognition in this two-way process. A lack of response will make us feel stressful and send us some very negative messages. Lack of response may mean we are not valued, that we have nothing to offer. It may produce powerful feelings of rejection. On the other hand, a favourable response sends us positive messages which contribute to our sense of self-worth. Recognition helps us to feel that we have something useful to contribute.

For example, you may have talked, smiled and given lots of attention to a small baby but have picked up very little from the baby's expression. Then one day the baby smiled. Do you remember how you felt? Can you remember your thoughts? You may have asked yourself whether or not he knew you from other people, or if he recognised your face or voice. The details of that first interaction will have been special. **Interaction** means 'having an effect upon each other'.

Now do Exercise 1.

In Exercise 1, by 'assumptions' I mean your opinion of what the people were like, what sort of images you had built up without having any information apart from what you could see.

On meeting people, we as care workers will need to create trust, to describe ourselves and our role to our clients. These may be difficult things to communicate and we may need to use all, or at least several, of the following ways:

- Talking
- Writing
- Body talk
- Use of space
- Surroundings

EXERCISE 1

Think of someone you meet or pass each day, where no words are spoken and no gestures exchanged. It may be someone near work,; in the street or at a bus stop, or someone you pass in a corridor.

Consider what you feel about them or what assumptions you may have made. Decide that, next time you encounter each other you will greet them. Say 'Hello', or 'Good Morning', or 'It's a lovely day'.

Think about the response you receive and how it made you feel. Did it alter your assumptions about the person?

WAYS OF COMMUNICATING

TALKING

If you have thoughts you want to express you can use words. These words become a spoken message which passes through the air and reaches someone's ears. The words are then sorted out by the listener's brain, and the listener reacts. The listener will then decide whether or not to respond, and the process begins again.

However, sometimes a *previous* message from you, or from a third person, is fitted together with your message. This alters the meaning of your message for the listener. *You* may think you are asking a simple, straightforward question but because the listener has already received other messages he does not respond in the way you expect, as in the following example:

'Mrs Jones, would you like to have something to eat now?'

'Go away! People are obsessed with food and always asking me to eat. I am fed up with it.'

Perhaps you are the fifth person in half-an-hour to ask Mrs Jones if she would like something to eat!

The tone of the voice, its volume or pace, will also alter the meaning of a message. Imagine someone slowly and carefully arriving at your door, and slowly and carefully saying:

'Please phone the Fire Brigade to come to Number 22 where the house is burning down and all the family are trapped.'

Would you realise, at first, how urgent the message was? A person's background, role or nationality may also produce variations we are not used to in volume, voice or pace. For instance, someone with a long career of authority in the army may continue to give loud, clear, concise messages when they return to civilian life.

Also, do not assume that the client speaks the same language as you. If he does speak in another language then think carefully about the best way to overcome this difficulty. A member of the client's family may speak English but it may not be possible to use him as interpreter if this would compromise confidentiality or offend another family member. For example, if you wanted to discuss a gynaecological issue such as menstruation with an Asian woman it would be unsuitable to use one of her sons as interpreter and could lead to acute embarrassment for both parties.

Some health authorities or social service departments have a list of interpreters; the local police may also have a list. However, make sure you have as much information as possible about the situation *before* enlisting the services of an interpreter – the situation may look more straightforward than it is. For example, a person from Stornaway may speak only in Gaelic; a woman from the Indian sub-continent may speak Gujarati, Punjabi or Bengali. Once you have all the facts you can speak to your supervisor, if necessary.

WRITING

We can also express our thoughts through the written word. Some people love letter writing; others never do it. Some letters are written in a way that reveals much about the writer; others give very little away. When you write a report it can be full of words but say very little that is useful. Other writing is a simple request:

> PLEASE LEAVE
> 3 PINTS OF MILK
> AND 6 EGGS
> ON TUESDAY

Notices and signs are other types of written words which simply inform.

BODY TALK

Appearance

If the listener is able to see, some messages will have been conveyed before words were spoken. The way you look will have helped the listener to make a quick assessment. A certain coloured overall or uniform may have helped to identify your role; if not, your clothes will have influenced what this person thought of you.

Figure 1
Who would you rather talk to?

Imagine meeting the people shown in Figure 1. You will have decided before you speak which one you would rather talk to. This opinion may be altered after you begin to exchange words, but the way you respond on looking at them is based on your previous experience – on messages passed down to you about this type of person. These messages may have come from your family, friends, and society in general, newspapers or television. Sometimes your response may not suit the person and, if you are unable to alter it you will have a problem communicating successfully with him.

Behaviour

Many 'body talk' messages will involve behaviour. Some people wave their arms about when they talk. Some walk slowly, and sit down with arms and legs stretched apart. Often you can guess which country they come from simply from this body talk.

Some body movements suggest a certain state of mind. A man pacing up and down, unable to sit still for long, smoking, wringing his hands, constantly checking the time: this has long been the accepted image of the father-to-be awaiting news of his baby's arrival. But time can change these images. You would be less likely to see this now because fathers can be present in the room when their babies are born. You would need to look for other ways in which anxiety is expressed in this setting.

USE OF SPACE

Animals regard their space as territory. A cat, for example, does not allow other cats into its garden, that is, its 'territory', and will probably drive them away. If we are describing this response in people we often use such terms as 'personal space'. You will be aware of changes in your own response if you have cared for people in a residential home and have then seen them in their own home, on their own ground. Most of us feel at ease in someone's living room, but less at ease in their bedroom as this is a more personal or private space.

This personal space is also something we take around with us and which influences how near we allow people to our bodies. Someone who leaves only two or three inches between you when talking may make you feel awkward. If you are on intimate terms with them it may feel comfortable, although that can also depend on *what* they are saying. Some people retreat if you stand too close as you talk to them. If we are not sensitive to people's personal space we may drive people away or risk an aggressive response.

Touch

Our use of 'body space' is closely linked to our attitudes to touch. Some people like being touched, others will feel it distasteful or a violation. Certain areas of the body must not be touched, as for some these areas are solely for sexual contact.

Other kinds of touch may be felt appropriate only to a certain age group. For example, you may pat a child on the head and say 'Thank you, you have been a good boy' because the child may have done something to please you, but if your Bank Manager pleases you with a loan you will not respond in the same manner.

Touch can be reassuring or a sign of hostility promoting confrontation. For example, someone pointing a finger at you may annoy you and make you angry. If the finger makes contact and taps your chest you may feel it is a violation of your body space and this could lead to violence.

If we separate body space into zones, and look at the functions which take place within these zones, then the issues involved in touching may become easier to understand (see Figure 2).

We've seen that your territory at home may include your room, your house, your land and you recognise the boundaries when they are encroached upon. But the zones illustrated in Figure 2 are not so precise and neither you, nor others, can see the boundaries so clearly. However, our feelings often send us messages about these zones.

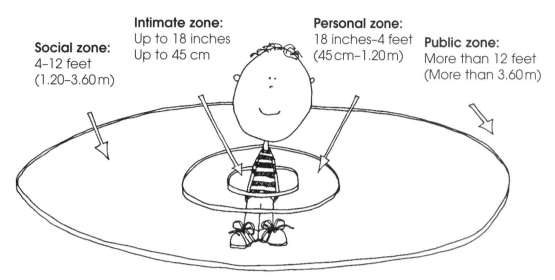

Figure 2
Zones around the body

Social zone:
4–12 feet
(1.20–3.60 m)

Intimate zone:
Up to 18 inches
Up to 45 cm

Personal zone:
18 inches–4 feet
(45 cm–1.20 m)

Public zone:
More than 12 feet
(More than 3.60 m)

Intimate zone

The intimate zone is the area up to 18 inches (45 cm) from your body. Within this zone you are close enough to another person to allow certain changes to occur. For example, you may whisper or talk softly – a much more intimate way of verbalising (expressing something in words). You may become aware of the person's body scent or heat. Within this space, sexual activity occurs so allowing strangers into this area can make people feel very uncomfortable.

The nature of your work as a care worker could mean you have to enter this space, this intimate zone, possibly without having had time to establish trust or even familiarity and this may cause discomfort between you and your client.

Personal zone

The personal zone is between 18 inches and 4 feet (45 cm and 1.20 m), approximately, and is used in a protective way. The boundaries expand or contract according to the setting you are in. In a large room you may be comfortable with the 18-inch space, but walking along a road you would probably be happier with the 4-foot distance. You usually limit entry into this space to people you already know.

Social zone

The social zone extends from 4 to 12 feet (1.20 m–3.60 m) and in this space touching is not possible. In some social settings, people may group themselves 4 feet apart, for example, a business meeting or a conversation in someone's living room.

Public zone

The public zone extends outwards from 12 feet (3.60 m) or more, and often occurs in large gatherings where a speaker addresses a group or an audience.

Now do Exercise 2

EXERCISE 2

Think about the following situations:

1. You are a woman waiting for a lift to get to the top of a building and you are in a hurry. The lift arrives at the 2nd floor where you are waiting. The doors open, the lift is almost full of men, and none of them gets out. You will have to squeeze your way in.

- Would you rather wait?

- If you go in, how will you position yourself in the lift and why?

- How will you feel in this situation?

2. You are a young man who takes the last seat on a crowded bus, next to a young lady unknown to you. As the bus keeps stopping more and more people get off. There are many empty seats around and only two people are left, sitting alone several seats away from you.

- Should you move?

- If not, will it make this lady anxious?

- Why should you move? You have done nothing wrong.

SURROUNDINGS

The type of house a person lives in and the furniture or decorations he uses will give you further messages about him. For example, you may see the objects in a person's home or surroundings as necessary or as rubbish. You may make assumptions if these objects are placed neatly or if they are scattered untidily. There may be too few of some things, too many of others.

You will probably jump to a conclusion about the person from his surroundings or at least form some impression about him. This may or may not be accurate. What appears to be disorder may have an explanation which could alter your opinion of the situation.

Even the type of building in which a person lives could make you decide what sort of person he is. It may be a flat, a terraced house, a semi-detached, or a detached house with a large garden. Initially, you will be influenced by such detail and may think you know what type of person lives in a house of that kind.

Assumptions are made on looking not only at the person but also at the whole scene, including the immediate surroundings, the area, and even the country, he lives in.

BARRIERS TO COMMUNICATION

Communication is a two-way process, like sharing, and the process described earlier in the section on 'Talking' may work well, but not always. Figure 3 looks in more detail at this process and identifies some of the barriers that may prevent good communication.

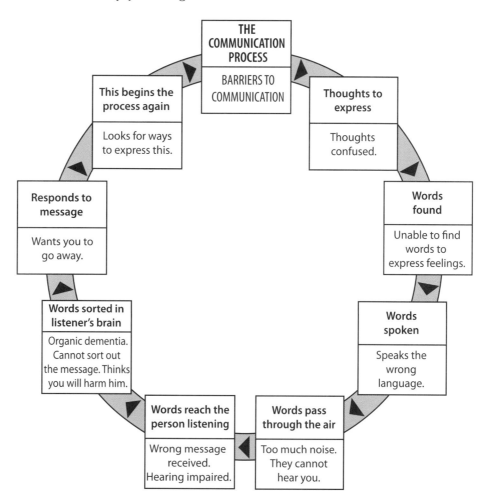

Figure 3
The communication process

WHAT WE SAY

Most of us will assume that the person to whom we are talking speaks our language. If there are outward signs (like dress) that he is from another culture or country we may need to talk clearly and carefully. But doing this could cause offence if the person has lived all his life in the country and speaks the language fluently. There are dangers in making assumptions because of skin colour or style of dress!

If the language spoken contains unfamiliar jargon or terminology, this can cause confusion or even be meaningless. For example:

> 'As I turned off the freeway this guy hit my fender, because I was freewheeling after running out of gas.'

> 'It's a real turn-off to me – it really screws me up – when people offload their hang-ups in my direction.'

These phrases may be easy enough for most young people to understand but a 90-year-old from a rural part of the country may have difficulty knowing what they mean.

7

WHERE WE MEET

The setting in which we are trying to communicate may not promote success for many reasons. There may be a **lack of privacy**, so that others not only hear what is being asked but would also hear the reply, for example, in the lounge of a residential home. Having to compete with a lot of **noise** may require the use of too much energy and may not be worth the effort. The distractions may hinder concentration and only half the dialogue may be heard. A **negative** or **non-response** may mean that the client feels you are not the appropriate person to deal with this problem.

WHO ARE WE SPEAKING TO?

It is important that the words we are saying reach the correct person. We must be sure that we identify the person we are talking to. For example, there could easily be confusion in a busy hospital ward if two patients have the same surname and one of them is mistakenly given information intended for the other.

IS THE MESSAGE BEING RECEIVED?

There may be many reasons why people do not respond to you in the way you expect:

- The listener may be deaf or have impaired hearing.
- He may already be occupied, be listening to someone else, or be preoccupied with his own thoughts.
- He may have decided he does not want to hear and may have switched off.
- He may be irritated by people in your role and therefore reject your approach.

Try to work out why your client responds as he does rather than assuming that he is just being awkward or disruptive.

How we respond

When you are introduced to someone, does it quickly emerge what his job is? Be honest and admit how often you think or say 'What does he do?' Look at the following list of different jobs:

minister of religion	bus driver
income tax inspector	teacher
company rep/salesman	cabinet minister
shop assistant	disc jockey
rent collector	actor
car salesman	writer
accountant	checkout operator
doctor	shoe salesman
housewife	

Pick out five individuals whom you could easily criticise, either because of their job or the people they work for. After selecting the five jobs, write down what type of person you think does this job. Then go on to Exercise 3. (For a discussion on stereotyping see page 15.)

EXERCISE 3

The following two people have the same problem. Describe how your approach to them could differ.

Person A

Miss Watson is a retired head teacher, becoming frail and unable to care for her personal hygiene as she previously did in a very meticulous way. You have been asked to visit her on a regular basis, to help her to have a bath and change her clothes.

Person B

Mr James is a retired miner and was a big, upright, strong man until recently. He is very disabled now and has difficulty moving about. As a result he is not able to attend to his personal hygiene. You are to visit him and help him to bath and change his clothes.

These are two different people with similar needs.
How will their previous roles alter your approach?

REVIEW

The various situations we encounter in everyday life contain many different examples of ways of communicating. As a care worker communication will be a major part of your work. You not only have to form some sort of relationship with your client but, along with the client, you have to find some way of identifying his needs. Some of these needs will be apparent, others will be difficult to express or identify because they produce distressing feelings or because the client does not have the vocabulary or skills to express himself to his best advantage.

Communication will be both verbal and nonverbal. Some things will be difficult for the client to disclose and we will look for 'body talk' messages. How the client responds to us, and to our entry into his personal zones, may help us to assess him. How we communicate will also depend on how he sees us in our role and as a person. The way we look, our accent, spoken language, country of origin, and the way we conduct ourselves will influence his responses to us.

The next chapter examines who we are in more detail and how much of 'us the person' becomes part of the role we take on as a care worker.

SUMMARY EXERCISES

1. Give three examples for each of the types of verbal communication listed below.
(One example of each type is given.)

Verbal communication that gives a warning.
'*Beware of falling rocks.*'

Verbal communication to influence another person.
'*Don't you think it would be a good idea to stop smoking?*'

Verbal communication that expresses feeling. '*I hate this place.*'

Verbal communication that is asking for help.
'*I will never manage to climb up these stairs.*'

2. Obtain from a health centre, doctor's surgery, housing office, post office or DSS office, a form claiming for some type of public service.

- Read it.
- Try to identity which parts of the form may be difficult to understand.
- List the words people may have difficulty with.
- Can you find a way of rewriting the words to make it more understandable?

3. Imagine a visit to a disabled person's house, where you help them to get up and dressed, give them breakfast and clean the house.

Describe the personal zones you will enter in that person's life, as you carry out your work.

2 Starting with yourself

CHOOSING TO BE A CARE WORKER

Why have you chosen to be a care worker? In thinking about the answer to this question you must acknowledge that you are acting in a caring capacity for *yourself* as well as for the client. You expect, and need, some satisfaction from your work.

We all have personal needs and helping others can experience personal growth. Personal needs such as self-worth, intimacy, status and being valued can be satisfied by taking on a caring role.

People working in the caring professions experience a great deal of satisfaction in seeing a client solving problems or finding a way to manage his life more effectively. To feel you had some part in this can be a great reward for persevering with a difficulty.

Care workers usually begin with some personal philosophy – their own beliefs and values. How you feel about the work is not easily hidden from the client and you will soon receive feedback telling you that the client is perceptive about your difficulties and feelings.

Carl Rogers (1961), writing about the qualities of care workers, talked about 'genuineness', that is whether or not care workers' words are consistent with their actions. For example, if a care worker says 'I am ready to hear what you have to say' and then is immediately distracted and does not listen, her behaviour is not consistent with her words.

This will rapidly become apparent to the client. It is important that you take a look at yourself, at what you bring to the work and what motivates you. Then explore the qualities necessary for a care worker so you can see where your strengths and weaknesses are and how these affect your relationship with the client.

In your attempts to communicate well it is important that you are flexible enough to take on different roles. Some areas of the work will demand a greater degree of intimacy with the client than others. You may find you have to work in a different way from the one you are used to and you must be willing to take some risk in order to make some impact. This will be of benefit to the client. He too may be seeking a new way to deal with his difficulties, a way that may mean changing some of his familiar and well-worn patterns of behaviour. If you show you are willing to try something new he may be more willing to confront his own need to change.

YOUR ROLE AS A CARE WORKER

Roles are the patterns of behaviour we expect from certain people. In your role as a care worker you will be expected to carry out various functions. Although the role may be new to you, you bring some skills into the work with you. Whatever these skills are, people will have certain expectations of you when they hear your job title, just as you have of others when you hear what their role is.

Some people will be surprised that your role allows you to undertake certain tasks; others will be equally surprised that your role does *not* allow you to undertake certain tasks and they will be unhappy about this. For example, a disabled lady was telling her home help how worried she was because her sister had not arrived to do her shopping. The home help told her she would always go to the local shops for if she wanted.

The client was very surprised to hear this – she had always thought the home help would only work in the house.

Now look at Exercise 4

EXERCISE 4

Think of two people whose job
involves more than you thought
at first.

Write down details.
For example, a librarian.

Communication between you, in your role as care worker, and your client will occur in some sort of formal structure. This encounter takes place because the client needs some kind of help and you are seen as having some kind of expertise, some kind of special knowledge. The client needs you for your ability to carry out the task. This puts you at an advantage and places the client in a vulnerable position.

Let us look at some of the assumptions you can make about the client and how this role/client relationship influences communication. There are certain principles within these assumptions which can act as a guide to the care worker.

ASSUMPTIONS

A need for help

At first you may not know what the client wants you to do to help. The client himself may not want to be helped. He may not even have initiated the call for help; this may have come from a son or a daughter, a parent or another relative, or a colleague at work. The client may feel you are an unnecessary intrusion and that he does not need you.

In rejecting you in your role as care worker the client may say:

> 'I do not need your help. I have nothing against you, you are a nice person but I do not need your help.'

If the motivation for help comes from a source other than the client you must remember this when you first meet him. Even when the client feels he *does* need help he will want to know all about you and check on whether or not you meet his expectations.

You will be closely scrutinised in this early encounter both in your role and as a person. You may only be offering someone a cup of tea, but they will find a way of discovering more about you, perhaps by saying:

> *'Thanks for the tea love. Is your husband looking after the kids?'*

A hidden problem

Another possibility you have to consider (especially after getting it wrong several times!) is that the real problem may not be the one stated. For example, many people will say:

> *'I feel really ill today', or 'I have a headache',*

rather than describe exactly what help they need, such as advice about a family problem.

If their thoughts are confused they may be unable to focus on their area of difficulty. Distractions, or an inability to concentrate, may prevent the client identifying what it is he needs. Admitting he needs help makes the client feel weak and helpless; he may feel it is more acceptable to say he is ill.

A loss of self-esteem

When the client is confronted with you in your role as a care worker it can erode his **self-esteem**.

"self-esteem"
Judgement or evaluation of your worth in relation to your ideal self and to the performance of others

A grasp of what self-esteem is about is important in our role of caring for other people, as well as for ourselves. When a client is confronted with a helper it may indicate he is weak, helpless or unable to sort himself out. In order to protect himself against further loss of self-esteem the client may present an aggressive or very assertive front. If we can recognise why the client responds in this way we will be supportive of him rather than critical.

The client needs to know something of your role but he will feel safer and more able to trust you if he has a glimpse of 'you the person' behind this role, a person with a lifetime of experiences.

KNOWING YOURSELF

The client and the care worker bring many personal traits into their relationship, including unique beliefs, attitudes, intelligence, behaviour and values. Somehow two people who may disagree over many of these aspects of life have to come together. They will also have to interact so that the client receives the help he needs. To allow this relationship to work more effectively, you will need some insight into yourself.

Before we look at some aspects of self-awareness **try Exercise 5** to find out more about the personal traits you bring to the interaction.

EXERCISE 5

Think of someone whom you feel is quite the opposite of you, perhaps someone you think you have little or nothing in common with. List the following personal traits and against each one write down how you are different from this person.

Unique beliefs

Attitudes

Intelligence

Behaviour

When you have done this ask yourself:

Is there one area where you could draw closer together with this person?

If you were to assume the role of being their helper how would you manage this?

SELF-AWARENESS

Three aspects of self-awareness are:

- Self-concept
- Beliefs and values
- Life experiences

Self-concept

Self-concept is the mixture of ideas, feelings and attitudes a person has about his own identity. It involves how you value yourself, how you see your capabilities and what you see as your limitations. How people value you and their opinion of you also play an important part in the development of self-concept. These values and opinions have a strong influence on you during your formative years. People who have suffered a lot of negative criticism in these years will have less confidence in their ability.

The care worker's feelings about herself will influence the way she interprets the communication and behaviour of her clients. Care workers with a positive self-concept will have faith in their own competence and will believe they have something useful to offer others.

These feelings of self-worth allow the care worker to respect and accept the worth of others. Positive self-worth can help a client accept criticism and see his difficulties as being only temporary. The person with a positive self-concept is less likely to be overwhelmed by difficulty and give up easily.

A negative self-concept in a care worker makes it difficult for her to see a way out of the situation. If she has often felt that the outcome will be to get it wrong she may think it is not worth trying too hard.

A care worker who feels bad about herself is less likely to be open with the client. She thinks it is better not to expose her vulnerability and weakness to others. She will be too timid to risk offering or looking for solutions because she might get it wrong and be seen to fail again. Therefore she will hold back and let the client make a mistake rather than risk both of them being wrong together.

It is important to remember that we cannot always get things right and there is not always a clear-cut right and wrong way to do things. You might prefer to proceed along the wrong path with another person and then return to find the right one with them, rather than make the journey alone.

The care worker who has a negative self-concept has another problem. As everyone is accountable for the standards of their work she may be less likely to seek out the help of colleagues or supervisors because this may expose her difficulties or inadequacies. It is very important for the care worker who feels this way to seek support from her care supervisor (in supervision sessions) or from someone else she can trust.

If we are to persuade our clients to believe in *them*selves, we must believe in *our*selves.

Beliefs and values

The client/care worker relationship is strongly affected by the beliefs and values of the people involved. We all tend to sit in judgement of others. At its worst, this could lead us to a complete rejection of clients, simply because they do not hold the same beliefs as we do.

For example, you may believe in absolute equality between men and women. Your client may be entirely submissive to her husband. You may find it hard not to let her know you think she is stupid to behave in this way. When such a difference emerges the result may be a rift in the client/care worker relationship. This may be a sign that you lack **empathy** with the client.

"empathy"
the ability to imaginatively share the feelings of another and communicate this understanding to him or her

A person's beliefs and values may be tied to their culture. **Culture** means learned patterns of values, beliefs, customs and behaviour that are shared by a group of interacting individuals. Each culture produces a set of rules or standards for behaviour which are passed from one generation to the next and which are subject to change. Cultural differences are much more easily recognised especially as more and more people live in multicultural societies. For this reason, you are more likely to have had to confront these difficulties than ignore them. Although it is important to be aware of cultural differences it is more important to approach each client as an individual. We must beware of **stereotyping** the client because of his background.

"stereotyping"
oversimplified mental picture or attitude

For example, the stereotype of a rugby player is a drunken singer of bawdy songs, who lacks sensitivity and is incapable of being gentle. Of course, we know that this is not the case, and that rugby players are as different from each other as the members of any other group. Being aware of only one particular part of that person's life may mean that we fail to gain an overall picture of him. The care worker's awareness of the values she has developed within her own culture, and of the values of her client's culture, will prevent misunderstanding.

Do you sometimes think in stereotypes?

Try Exercise 6

EXERCISE 6

Write down what you think is the stereotype of the following:

An income tax inspector

A young female hairdresser

A racing car driver

A police constable

A maths teacher

A car salesman

A vicar's wife

A railway porter

You can make this more fun by being more extreme. For example, for police constable you could write – All policemen begin by saying: 'HELLO, HELLO, HELLO, WHAT'S ALL THIS THEN?' Humour often gives clues as to what you really think.

Life experiences

The care worker may bring personal problems to her relationship with the client. She will certainly bring experiences of past difficulties resolved, possibly even the same difficulties as her client. For example, you may currently be coping with an awkward teenage daughter who is persistently argumentative and wants to stay out until the early hours of the morning. If the client you are working with is a teenage girl you may feel angry towards her and demand she considers her parents' feelings more than she is doing. But if you take this attitude she may then view you, the care worker, as 'just another parent'. It is important that you recognise your own problems and make sure that you have a non-judgemental attitude towards your client, as well as towards yourself, for having the problem.

HOW MUCH DO YOU SHARE?

The client needs a glimpse of 'you the person' behind the role. Some care workers will be working in conditions that allow relationships to develop. This may be one of the major attractions of the work. As communication becomes easier, and more is shared between you and the client, a different picture of each of you emerges. This sharing is called **self-disclosure**.

SELF-DISCLOSURE

Opinions vary considerably about how much of yourself you share with, or disclose to, the client. On the positive side, those supporting self-disclosure say that it gives the client an opportunity to glimpse the person behind the role, so he can see there is more to you than the tasks you have to perform. This can reassure the client that other people have concerns, perhaps similar to his own.

Those who oppose self-disclosure argue that it encourages the client to view the relationship with too much intimacy. The relationship then becomes one of friendship rather than a useful working relationship. Another worry about self-disclosure is that the worker can fill the conversation with talk about herself rather than about the client. The focus then remains on the unresolved personal problems of the *worker* instead of on the care of the *client*.

Now do Exercise 7.

EXERCISE 7

Make a list of points for and against self-disclosure in care workers. For example:

FOR	AGAINST
It reassures the client that he is being treated as an individual	The client may come to depend too much on the care worker's decisions instead of making his own.

See whether there are more points for it than against it.

If you work in a more personal way with the client how much do you disclose and in what way? Do you show your own feelings and emotions? If you are going to be seen as a real person you must share feelings. Strong feelings shared, whether planned or otherwise, can have a marked impact on your client.

Some traditional approaches have suggested that you should remain neutral when responding to a client. This prevents you expressing any more than a mild degree of affection or caring, irritation or anger. On the other hand, it has been suggested that if the care worker responds spontaneously to the client this leads to greater self-awareness for the client.

Many clients have become isolated from others because of their disability. People may have ceased to respond to them naturally in order to protect them from some of the difficulties of the outside world and prevent further conflict or stress. But this has a negative side – it protects clients from some of the realities of life and puts them in an unrealistic world. By being more spontaneous, the care worker may give the client a more realistic outlook on life, and prepare him for some of its difficulties.

DEVELOPING A PARTNERSHIP

The relationship between you, the care worker, and the client should be a partnership. Then the responsibility for care and for making progress in meeting the client's needs is shared. Rather than you being the person with all the knowledge or expertise, you will regard the client as the expert who ultimately knows most about his own needs.

If the client keeps an active role in any decisions made about him the balance of power between you both is controlled. He should not consider himself a passive recipient of what you have to offer. You do not want him to feel the helpless victim of the care system, but rather to feel a sense of retaining personal power. With the partnership philosophy, the client will learn that decisions are not made for him, but that he has some choice.

3 Getting to know each other

YOUR CLIENT AS A PERSON

Our work is with real people, who need us to communicate with them as part of the care we provide. We need to find out what our client is like, to identify the individual and not just, for example, his physical needs. One way of doing this is to use the idea of **holism,** an approach to people which takes account of the whole person, not just one part.

"holism"
a philosophy which looks at how parts work together – rather than looking at each part separately, in isolation

HOLISM

Holistic principles are a helpful way of examining human dynamics, or 'what makes a person tick', because they work on the five **dimensions** of the person:

- Physical
- Emotional
- Intellectual
- Social
- Spiritual

This approach to helping an individual can be used by workers in other fields – teachers, personnel officers, prison staff – as well as the caring professions. This is because, in whatever capacity you approach a client, holism makes common assumptions.

The major assumption is that everyone has unrealised potential – unused talents – and that this is best developed through self-responsibility and self-help. The holistic approach recognises that all aspects of a person are significant and considers how these can work together to help the whole person. If we deal with any one aspect in isolation we are left with an incomplete view of the client.

The following are some examples of how we fragment people by labelling them:

> *'That arthritic old lady in room ten.'*

> *'Harry who sits in the chair near the door and won't talk.'*

> *'The appendix in bed six.'*

> *'The child who screams all the time.'*

Now look at Exercise 8

We often have to begin with a narrow or ill-defined image of the client because of lack of knowledge. One of the thrills of working with people is seeing that image open out to reveal more. Who knows what will be revealed?

EXERCISE 8

How have you labelled people in your own neighbourhood? Because your knowledge of them is incomplete you use what is obvious. For example:

'The thin chap two doors away with the estate car'.

List four more examples of this type of description.

ATTITUDES AND RESPONSES

Three things which can affect our client's response to us are:

● Regard for the client

● Pace of speech

● Use of time

Regard for the client

You show regard in the way you express your respect for the client. Carl Rogers says that this regard should be unconditional – no strings – and positive. This means accepting the client just as he is without judging him. The client retains his dignity and worth as a human being. Rogers calls this 'Unconditional Positive Regard', meaning your help is offered without pre-conditions. If you are only offering help on the condition that your client changes in some way, he may say, for example:

'We used to get on so well but just lately you keep asking me to do things I do not like. I may have to find someone else to help me if you keep this up.'

You may feel that Unconditional Positive Regard is a 'tall order.' It may be that, at some time in the relationship, you will need to express some of your own approving or disapproving attitudes. We have already said that the client needs a glimpse of you the person, of your individuality, but we need to consider where we draw the line, in other words how we implement Unconditional Positive Regard.

In showing regard the attitude we are trying to convey is:

'I neither approve nor disapprove of what you are saying. I want you to express yourself freely. I respect your right to feel as you please.'

This does not mean the person can act out these feelings in a way that harms you. Later in the relationship the regard can become more conditional. If the care worker expresses more of her own approving or disapproving attitudes this may reinforce or reduce certain behaviour in her clients, as in the following example:

20

> **EXAMPLE**
>
> You meet a young client who is angry and abusive. You may begin by saying:
>
> *'Tell me what is upsetting you. It will be better if you talk about it, rather than kicking or hitting the wall.'*
>
> You then listen to a torrent of abuse and strong language as he expresses how distressed he is. If he apologises for the way he is talking you could say:
>
> *'Don't worry, go on, tell me.'*
>
> You are giving him permission to share, with no conditions. You are giving him respect and showing regard for the way he feels.
>
> Over the next few days, whenever something goes wrong or he is unhappy about something, he uses abusive language. Now you can impose conditions. You tell him that he cannot keep behaving this way as it offends people and shows them no respect or regard. You attempt to modify his behaviour so he can live more harmoniously with people and not erect barriers to useful communication.

In this example, you began with an Unconditional Positive Regard for the client but eventually imposed conditions.

Pace of speech

Pace means the rate of progress at which we communicate. Pace can vary considerably for different clients. It is important that you are able to stay with the client, to keep up with him or wait for his understanding to catch up with what you are saying. If you are one step ahead of him all the time he can become distracted and have difficulty concentrating.

The pace of a communication can be altered by the:

- nature of the subject matter
- age and intelligence of the client
- client's physical condition

If he is describing what occurred at a time of crisis he may show he is under pressure because he is speaking rapidly and his thoughts are disordered. For example:

> *'I have lost my door key. How can I get in the house? My friend will be round for her tea any time now. She will think I am stupid because it is not ready. Quick – I've just remembered the pan was on the stove. There was a fire over there last week after the same thing. Why are you just standing there? Do something! I should have started to pack my case as well for my holiday next week. Everything's a mess.'*

Young children use a different pace. They search carefully, within their limited vocabulary, for words to express what they want. You would expect the pace to be much slower here, as you would with an adult who has a learning difficulty. The pace set by the client forms a pattern. You must follow this pattern until you can take part in the conversation. Sometimes you will need to stay with the pace set until you can direct the conversation towards an appropriate focus for providing help and this means you must have a goal to aim at.

The pace of a client's conversation indicates how the client is tolerating some of the stresses and tensions caused by his situation. For example, the lady with the missing door key in the previous example is providing far more information than is needed to sort out the immediate problem.

Use this information in Exercise 9.

EXERCISE 9

Rewrite the account of the lady with the lost door key, break into the monologue, or work out where you can begin to help. This will involve helping the client to remove unnecessary information and concentrate on what will be useful. Describe how this might happen.

Use of time

When you are communicating with the client time can either be very useful or something that adds to your stress levels! At times the client may think that he is the only one with a problem and will be unable to grasp that you may be needed elsewhere. He begins to tell you something but does not finish the story because you have to leave. This is frustrating for you both. However, if you begin by saying you only have half-an-hour the client will find some way of saying what he has to say within that period, even if it means leaving out some detail. This way you will have some idea what the problem is. Most people, if told how much time is available, manage to make the best use of it. You may even offer a certain amount of time and then decide you will have to give more, and your offer will be valued highly by the client. Remember, it is not necessarily an advantage to have plenty of time to spend with a client – how you use the time is what counts.

Try Exercise 10.

EXERCISE 10

Think of an encounter where you were glad of only having very little time. Write an account of the incident.

MAKING CONVERSATION

BEGINNINGS AND ENDINGS

Some of the greetings or 'beginnings' we exchange may not take people very far into a conversation. They reveal very little about the person or about what is happening. Nevertheless, they serve a useful purpose because they add some formal structure in which to work.

You may pass somebody on a walk in the park and nod at them, or just smile and say 'Hello'. You may not do this intending to open a conversation but simply to reassure each other that you are both friendly.

Many of these exchanges are with people you know. If you are out shopping and see a colleague from work a nod acknowledges that a relationship exists. The other person may be insulted if they are not acknowledged.

These openings and greetings may *seem* insignificant but they have a great influence on what we think of people – and on what they think of us. A failure in this area can cause deep offence. Greetings are powerful statements about the state of a relationship. Refusing to greet or acknowledge someone, keeping a blank expression and not looking them in the eye, can have a lasting effect.

Some people believe that all adult clients should be addressed as Mr, Mrs or Miss, because doing so conveys respect for their status as adults. If this seems extreme then so is addressing all clients by their first name. To begin formally, with Mr, Mrs or Miss allows the *client* to have control over any move towards informality, if they wish.

Many Western people still feel happier with the formal handshake when introducing themselves. This provides an opportunity to touch the person and perhaps convey some other feeling. If the hand is cold and clammy, for instance, it may be a sign of extreme anxiety.

Think about this in more detail in Exercise 11.

EXERCISE 11

Make a list of words that describe a handshake, such as 'firm' or 'limp'

See how many ways you find, and then think of the person they describe. It is surprising how often the description 'a wet or dead fish' turns up on this list.

A handshake gives you the chance to name yourself and say who you are, that is, what your role is. At this point you may decide to use your first name with your surname as this usually implies that the client can use your first name.

From an early age we receive strong messages about how important first meetings are, especially if we want to create a good impression. First meetings are therefore a source of anxiety; we fear we will be at the mercy of someone who is bound to make judgements about us without knowing much about us. We often come away thinking 'I wonder what she thought of me?'

Sometimes we may be introduced by a third party who provides a few personal details, as if vouching for our credibility. How serious you are about

23

the introduction, and how much attention you give to it, will be closely watched – a frivolous attitude or the wrong tone of voice can alter the effect of the opening.

Endings are equally important. If you are working in a businesslike manner, the client may relax after the formal ending and begin to talk more informally.

If you have talked to a client to offer some help or set up some work, and have agreed on this, you may end with a formal handshake. For many, this kind of handshake signifies agreement and satisfaction at having concluded a transaction. The offer of a handshake at the end of the transaction conveys this feeling. A quick handshake, and withdrawing the hand straight away, may indicate disagreement.

Now do Exercise 12.

EXERCISE 12

Over the next two days, write two short accounts of how you began and ended some of your meetings with other people, what produced difficulties and what helped to make the transaction more manageable.

THE CONVERSATION

When we converse we begin with an opening, structure what happens in the middle, and close with an ending. The beginning will involve finding the correct time to open the conversation. The appropriate time for this will depend on the nonverbal clues you pick up from your client. A smile, or nod of the head, may indicate that someone is willing to be approached and that you may begin.

Conversations involve:

- Talking and tone of voice
- Listening and hearing
- Taking turns to speak

Talking and tone of voice

When people talk to us we are not only influenced by the content of the conversation but also by the tone and use of the voice. Voices vary tremendously and they are interpreted in many ways. For example:

'He had a deep, sexy voice'

'She has a voice which commands attention'

'Her voice irritates me.'

We recognise some people immediately from the sound of their voice.

Try Exercise 13.

EXERCISE 13

Think about people to whom you speak regularly on the telephone. Make a list of:

People you always know from the sound of their voice, without an introduction

People whose identity you have to check out, perhaps because they sound like another person.

Look at both lists. Do those with distinctive voices possess stronger personal characteristics than the others?

We perceive voices differently according to the sex of the speaker. We may comment on a woman's voice for its qualities of 'sensitivity', 'humour' or 'drive'. The qualities noted in a man's voice will be connected with physical and emotional power. Soft, quiet voices that take a great deal of effort to hear are often associated with shy, introverted people.

Listening and hearing

How do you show that you are a good listener? Let us begin by looking at some professionals, those who make a living as chat show hosts on television. **Look at Exercise 14.**

EXERCISE 14

Arm yourself with a clipboard and paper, and watch the chat show host when he is talking. List the things he does to indicate he is paying attention to the guest.

What the chat show host does may appear exaggerated but he has to make everything obvious for the viewer. He uses lots of smiles, nods of the head, clear movements forward or away, and grimaces.

You should not respond in this way to your clients but it points the way to using listening skills. For example, if your client is deaf, responding in this exaggerated way will be particularly useful. Also, you must look at the person you are listening to; this is most important when they begin to speak and when they are finishing. They will need some signal that you are 'on the same wavelength' at this important stage of the conversation.

Now do Exercise 15.

EXERCISE 15

Try to open a conversation with someone, without looking at them. How do you feel? Imagine how they feel.

A smile and a nod show you are following a conversation. A smile is not only used to indicate humour but also sympathy and discomfort so it can be used in many situations.

We have also developed responses which are not words but noises, such as:

'Mmm...'

'Huh ...' and

'Aah...'

You can probably think of more sounds like those yourself. Some words encourage the client to go on and indicate your enthusiasm for more. For example:

'Really?'

'What a thing to say!'

'That's amazing!'

'Fancy!'

'I can't wait to hear the outcome of this!'

You can also use questions and answers, which we will look at in more detail on page 27.

The way you sit also conveys messages about your attentiveness and interest. At school do you remember being told to 'Sit up and pay attention!' because you were looking sloppy? Good listeners do not slide down in their chairs or fidget around.

Listening is not a positive event but involves the way you use your whole body.

Taking turns to speak

Taking turns is not as easy as it sounds. You cannot assume it will happen just because conversation is a two-way process. A delicate balance has to be maintained to keep a conversation flowing and avoid the feelings of discomfort which can be caused by long pauses or silences.

People often feel they could have said more or that they did not get a fair share of the conversation. Obviously, you cannot both speak at the same time but there will be short periods when words overlap. If someone stops speaking it may not be your turn to speak – the other person could be searching for the right words or thinking of an answer. Eventually we learn to use these pauses and if we ignore them we are sent firm messages telling us to stop or wait.

Not only do we learn to use the pause – which may only be a few seconds – but we also learn to anticipate the need to speak. Some familiar phrases anticipate a fairly short reply, allowing us to move in again quite quickly. For example:

'Have we met before?'

This question can be used simply to clarify the relationship and may not require a long, complicated answer – even so, you may still get one!

'Taking turns' also involves knowing when to interrupt. Two, three or more people can do this successfully without the conversation becoming meaningless, for example, in a discussion during a committee meeting. Holding a conversation is an everyday event which works on many different levels. We can exercise some control over our conversations if we:

- plan what to say

- try to understand what others are saying

- become aware of the most suitable time to finish.

DEVELOPING CONVERSATIONAL SKILLS

There are various ways of structuring our conversations:

- Using questions

- Restating

- Validating

- Confrontation

- Reflection

- Ventilation

USING QUESTIONS

In the process of caring for others, you will need to ask questions. These are commonly divided into two types: **closed** and **open**.

Closed questions are for obtaining specific pieces of information and can only be answered in one way. For example:

> Qu: *'Where do you live?'*
>
> Ans: *'In Wales/Liverpool/Hawick.'*
>
> Qu: *'Are you married?'*
>
> Ans: *'Yes/No/I used to be.'*
>
> Qu: *'What is your date of birth?'*
>
> Ans: *'July 15th 1960.'*

The **open** or **open-ended question** has a less predictable reply. It cannot usually be answered by a single word such as 'yes' or 'no'. The answers invited are usually longer and more involved, and include the person's opinions and feelings. For example, there are no straightforward or obvious answers to these questions:

> Qu: *'Can you tell me why you dislike living here?'*
>
> Qu: *'When do you find it difficult getting to know people?'*
>
> Qu: *'What are you worrying about?'*

Now try Exercise 16.

EXERCISE 16

Devise a short questionnaire about the area in which you live. Make two lists of four or five questions. The first, to obtain some straight facts, should consist of closed questions. The second list should contain open-ended questions to explore the person's opinion of the area.

Find someone to put the questions to. Summarise the differences in the length and detail of the answers you receive.

As you get to know your client you are likely to use more open-ended questions, particularly if you are exploring the way he feels. These will be useful in encouraging him to share his views or feelings and will give him the chance to give his own account of something, to tell his story. Open-ended questions invite a unique response so they can be used to check how the client feels about the advice, information or care he has been given. They allow him a greater amount of freedom to respond.

For example, this closed question:

'Don't you think she is a very narrow-minded person?'

invites the answer 'yes' or 'no' but the open question:

'What is your opinion of her?'

allows the client to deal with the question from any point of view.

RESTATING

We can use restating to help the client understand himself. Restating means repeating back to the client, using his choice of words. Doing this may increase the client's awareness of exactly what he is saying. For example:

Client: *'Too many people are in and out of **my** room'*

Care worker: *'Too many people ...'*

Client: *'Yes, I never get any peace.'*

Care worker: *'When you say "too many people are in and out of **my** room" do you mean you do not need them all, or they are not necessary? When you say "**my** room" in that way what do you really mean?'*

Restating should be done calmly, without trying to pressurise the client into gaining more insight. The client might think that the care worker was being aggressive if the previous example was restated as:

Client: *'Too many people are in and out of my room.'*

Care worker: *'What do you mean, "my room"?'*

Restating can be irritating if it is not used thoughtfully.

VALIDATING

Validating is an important way of accepting the client's view of a situation and should help him feel he is understood. You may not necessarily agree with his perception of something, but you are saying you understand why he sees it in that way. For example:

> Client: '*The noise outside here last night was terrible. You would not believe how serious it was. I nearly rang the police.*'

> Care worker: '*I'm not surprised you felt upset if the noise was so bad. You must have felt pushed to the limit if you nearly rang the police. What do you think it was all about?*'

In this example, the care worker validates the appropriateness of the client's feelings and his response. She quickly follows this up with a question that explores the difficulty further. The client should be able to sense the care worker's interest and her acceptance of what he said. The care worker's response also conveys the subtle suggestion that although the client responded to the noise in this way others might have felt differently.

A negative response that invalidated the client's feelings, would have been:

> Client: '*The noise outside here last night was terrible. You would not believe how serious it was. I nearly rang the police.*'

> Care worker: '*Come on now. It can't have been half as bad as that.*'

CONFRONTATION

Often, the word 'confrontation' is used to indicate an aggressive or hostile response. In the context of communication skills, **confrontation** means an encounter between two people in which one sets out to encourage the other to face something. It may be something painful, or objectionable, or difficult to deal with. You assume that the client does not want to deal with the issue and that you need to encourage him to confront it.

Confrontation can provoke anger, so it is only used after careful thought if a positive outcome is worth the risk. There are no definite rules as to when to do it. Your decision is based on your judgement and what you know about the client or the difficulties of the situation. For example:

> Care worker to client: '*Whenever I ask you if I can arrange to take you shopping for clothes, you change the subject. Is there some reason why you don't want to go?*'

The client could give a variety of answers:

> '*I have no money – it's all gone on cigarettes*'

or

> '*I'd rather go with someone else. I didn't want to hurt your feelings.*'

Those who use this type of confrontation believe it promotes a healthier relationship with the client because it makes the client more accountable for his behaviour.

REFLECTION

Reflection should state clearly what the client is saying about his difficulties or feelings. The difference between reflection and restating is that you do not have to use the client's words, you can find some other way of helping him describe how he is feeling. However, you need to reassure him you know this is how he feels now, but you also know he may not always have felt like this and may not do so in the future. For example, the client may say:

29

> 'My neighbours keep calling in saying they want to help, but they just ask me questions. We all know what they want, don't we?'

Your response could be:

> 'It sounds to me as if you think they're not much help, and that all they're doing is trying to find out about your personal life.'

Reflecting is a way of showing the client that you understand how he is feeling. As you reflect his feelings back in words and expression he also knows you are paying attention to him. You are working hard at getting to a real understanding of the client. **Now do Exercise 17.**

EXERCISE 17
Try to remember a situation where someone responded to you with a blank expression or a flatness of mood. Write down the way it made you feel.

VENTILATION

In the context of communication ventilation is used to describe a response to particularly difficult situations. Ventilating allows the client to speak freely about his thoughts and feelings. It is an effective way of reducing tension and anxiety because it allows the client to return to a calmer state of mind. By reliving what happened, and how he felt, the client may come to see the experience in a different way. For example:

> Client: 'I was burgled last night. Before I could do anything he escaped. I'm stupid – I left the window open. I feel awful, so helpless. I didn't even see him.'

> Care worker: 'I wonder what you'd say to him if you did see him? What would you say about the effect he has on people?'

> Client: 'First, I'd want to hit him. Then I'd ask him how he would like it if someone came to his house and touched his personal things and took away property that had special memories attached to it, like gifts from friends and relatives. It makes you feel weak and helpless. As if you've no control over your life. I hate him. I've never wanted to hurt anyone before but I'd lock him away and lose the key. After what I've suffered. He's left me scared. I know now how awful it is to be alone.'

This dialogue shows that a few words can 'open the door' for powerful feelings to be released. The client is then able to name and understand these difficult emotions.

REVIEW

We have looked at brief descriptions of the skills we all use in communicating and which we can improve for the benefit of our client and ourselves. These techniques allow us a better understanding of our client and through them the client is also able to reach a clearer understanding of himself and his situation.

SUMMARY EXERCISES

1. You meet a young man who has just travelled seven miles to a factory on the chance they might have vacancies for work. He had heard they often had and, as he'd been out at work for a year, it appeared worth a try. However, he was sent away without a hearing because he had no appointment. He was not given any chance to discuss the job situation.

Make a list at words to describe how he might feel.

2. It is important to remember that people do not always respond as we expect them to. Using the words on the list you have just made, describe three different ways in which the young man may have responded to the situation he was in.

---

4 Special difficulties

HOW WE USE OUR SENSES

Individuals are continually communicating with the environment. This ability develops from an early age, along with 'sensory apparatus' such as our eyes and ears. A baby's first nerve endings develop through his skin and send messages back to the brain about touch, temperature and pain. As the system becomes more refined the child learns he is separate from the environment and can use his senses to gain his knowledge of the world. By receiving and responding to clues from the environment the child learns to adapt to these responses. Have you watched a young child when he first sees or touches a dog or cat? He shows a sense of wonder, curiosity and surprise: 'This is what cat is, and this is how it feels'. The child gains a new experience and adds to his knowledge of the environment.

Our sensations are an important part of our ability to interact with the environment. If these sensations are impaired in any way we feel a sense of disorder. We would have to adapt to the fact that the clues we receive from the environment have altered.

This adapting is not easy. Over the years we develop successful and familiar patterns for receiving and dealing with sensory messages. Now, either through sudden or gradual changes, we have to develop some new way of communicating.

Look at Exercise 18.

EXERCISE 18

Ideally, you should be at a children's party for this familiar game. You may have to throw a party to watch it happen! If not, simply play again the game of 'Pinning the Tail on the Donkey'.

Draw a large donkey, without a tail, on a board or piece of paper. Make a separate tail on another piece of paper and attach a drawing pin or some Blu-Tak. The idea is to blindfold each child, spin him around and ask him to pin the tail to the donkey.

The immediate response of the blindfolded person in the game 'Pin the Tail' is to stretch out his arms in front of him. He does this so he can obtain some clues to his environment through the sensation of touch now that he cannot obtain clues through vision. This illustrates an adaptive process – a different way of obtaining information.

Clients may experience disruption to some of their body systems when they have to leave familiar surroundings. For example, the hospital environment may change a person's sensory input, that is, the messages received by his senses. This may be made worse if illness has already damaged or altered his systems of communication.

32

In this chapter, we will explore:

● changes in sensory input – 'sensory alteration'

● how this interferes with the communication process

● how we may need to adapt.

The care worker will adapt to the client's particular needs and the client will use different systems to receive the messages.

SENSORY PERCEPTION

We 'find our bearings' in the environment through our ability to receive and organise **sensory stimuli**. The reception and organisation of stimuli is known as **sensory perception**. This reception of stimuli, and their journey through nerve pathways, is part of the **nervous system** (see Figure 4). This system can, and does, go wrong.

Our brain makes sense of the messages

Messages from our senses travel along nerve pathways

We may not receive a suitable number of clues from our environment. Too few clues is known as sensory deprivation; too many clues as sensory overload.

Figure 4
Sensory Perception

People who are imprisoned and in solitary confinement can suffer from sensory deprivation. The amount of sensory input they receive is below the individual's level of tolerance. The tolerance level is the range each person has for tolerating every type of sensation, while still functioning well and being comfortable. For example, your tolerance level for sound may be different from that of a teenage son or daughter! If the input exceeds the top range of tolerance, this is known as sensory overload.

Now do Exercise 19.

EXERCISE 19

What would cause you sensory deprivation and sensory overload?

List five examples of each.

ASSESSING FOR SENSORY ALTERATIONS

If your client has a communication problem caused by sensory alteration you will have to identify the source of the problem. With some clients this will be obvious but with others you will have to use your powers of observation and perhaps ask some questions. The answers will come from the client and his environment, and will help you adapt your method of communication to suit the client. Your observations and questions will be about some of the following areas:

Sensory status

Look at the status of the client's sight, hearing, smell, taste and touch.

- Does the client see and hear well?
- Does he use corrective devices such as spectacles, a hearing aid, or a magnifying glass?
- Can he discriminate between different tastes and smells?
- Does he feel changes in temperature, feel pain or know the difference between sharp and blunt?
- Does he define the place of objects in his surroundings, that is, know how near or far objects are in relation to himself?

Consciousness level

- Is the client fully conscious, drowsy, unconscious?
- Is there some disease or injury of the nervous system? For example, if someone has previously had a stroke he may have lost the sensation of touch down one side of his body. A client with a spinal cord injury may have lost sensation and function because of damage to the spinal cord.

Motor status

Look at the kinds of activity or movement the client is capable of.

- Is the client capable of independent movement?
- Is the change a result of paralysis, or a plaster cast, or is he immobilised for some other reason?

Cognitive status

Consider any patterns you have noticed in the client's thinking.

- Can he process information and respond to it appropriately?
- Is his memory intact?
- Is he able to plan?
- Is his judgement impaired?
- Is the client **orientated** in time, place and person?

"orientated"
able to correctly relate
the self to time, place
and person

Communication status

- Is the ability to communicate within the normal range?

34

- Can the client begin normal speech, understand it, and respond to verbal clues?

- Can the client read and write, and follow simple instructions?

Age and development level

- Is the client's developmental level appropriate to his age?

- What is appropriate for this client?

Psychological status

- Is the client self-reliant?

- How does he cope – is he angry, anxious or irritable?

Use of drugs

- Is the client taking any drugs or alcohol which could impair his awareness of what is happening around him?

Specific stressors known

- This could be an illness which reduces the amount of oxygen to the brain, such as heart disease or respiratory disease. It could also include pain, toxic status or isolation.

Try Exercise 20.

EXERCISE 20

Think of someone you know with a longstanding illness which has disabled them in some way. Would any of the nine previous factors cause difficulties in communication for them?

How would this knowledge alter the way you communicate with them?

You need not go through this process with every client but, if you know the process, you will be able to observe your client's communication problems and make appropriate judgements.

VISUAL IMPAIRMENT

Most blind people are in the older age groups. Their disability may range from slight impairment to total loss of vision. Some have perception of light and dark only; others have impairment in their field of vision, that is they see only what is central or only what is on the edge of their field of vision.

Blind people have major difficulties because of limitations in their:

- range and variety of experiences

- mobility

- relationship with the environment.

These limitations are caused because a person who cannot see must use touch and movement to gain experience of the world. They may not perceive objects which are too large or too small.

Many blind people feel that their most serious difficulty is restricted movement because this leads to reliance on aids or on other people, particularly in unfamiliar areas. Sight gives us a sense of our place in the environment and helps us to control ourselves in it. Blind people may withdraw from others, or others withdraw from blind people because they cannot respond to the glances, smiles, frowns and other visual gestures which are an important part of communication.

It is not only in non-verbal communication that the blind are at a disadvantage. Their inability to read and communicate in other conventional ways, such as writing and drawing, means fewer opportunities for learning. Personal care, housework, cooking and home maintenance all take on another dimension. If you are elderly and have other physical limitations, life can be even more frustrating.

Exercise 21 will help you appreciate some of the problems.

EXERCISE 21

Think of an average day, with nothing out of the ordinary happening. Perhaps you could look at the first hour after waking up on a working day.

Make a list of the simple, everyday tasks you perform, and alongside this list write down what you are looking at as you perform them. Then, remove the list of what you see and imagine performing the tasks without sight.

As a care worker you could be helping your client adjust to a major change in his life. He may withdraw or feel disbelief, anger, depression and embarrassment at his own helplessness. You are likely to be a key person in his continuing and painful adjustment to his disability.

Asking for help in carrying out normal, routine, day-to-day tasks is frustrating. Blind people experience being ignored, shouted at, or being referred to rather than addressed directly but when with friends, blind people are sensitive to being treated differently, particularly at the onset of their blindness. You should be able to inform your client of any help available in his area, such as talking books or newspapers.

The following may be helpful as guidelines for communicating with blind people:

- Talk in a normal tone of voice.

- Introduce yourself with each contact unless you are well known to the person. If in residential care or hospital, knock on the door before entering.

- Do not avoid common expressions such as 'I see what you mean'.

- Explain any activity occurring in the room, or what you will be doing.

- When you are leaving the room, let the person know so that he is not left talking to someone who is not there.

HEARING LOSS

Hearing loss ranges from difficulty in understanding words, through hearing only certain sounds, to total deafness. Care workers obviously need to be able to communicate with these clients and encourage them to seek medical advice about the impairment, if they have not already done so.

The signs of hearing loss are:

- Failure to respond to verbal communication

- Inappropriate response to verbal communication

- Loud speech

- Abnormal awareness of sounds

- Strained facial expression, or puzzled look when a response is expected

- Leaning forward or tilting head when listening

- Always needing to have conversation explained

- Faulty speech articulation

- Behavioural clues, such as changing the topic of conversation or beginning some activity to cover up the defect

Some of the signs of hearing loss cause people to withdraw from social situations and become anxious. They may have to cope with feelings of isolation, stress and inadequacy. The following suggestions can be useful in all types of hearing loss:

Start the communication with light on your face. It will help the client to see your expression and your lips.

- Get the client's attention by raising an arm or a hand.

- Speak clearly but do not overemphasise the words.

- Talk directly to the client, facing him. Do not shout, as this may not necessarily be helpful – it may cause distortion and be too loud for people with hearing damage.

- At first you may not be understood. Some words are difficult to see in speech reading. 'White' and 'Red' are often difficult to perceive in this way.

- Write out names and other words which are not understood.

- The client may have a better ear, if so talk to this side.

- Certain mannerisms cause problems in communication. Sitting with your hand over your mouth, or resting your jaw on a hand, may prevent full movement. People who chew gum at the same time as talking can cause confusion for the listener.

- Use more than one syllable to communicate answers; say what subject you are going to talk about first, before going on to details.

- Non-response or inattention does not always mean lack of understanding. Look for signs of tiredness.

- People who are hard of hearing depend on facial clues for being accepted. A careless glance or expression can be quickly noticed.

- Encourage the use of hearing aids.

- Avoid little asides to others in the group. It is easy for those with hearing difficulties to feel left out in this situation.

Good communication is possible. These skills can be learned quickly; using them helps to reassure hearing-impaired people who often feel they are being avoided. Make sure you know what the local community can offer your hearing-impaired client, for instance, there may be a club he can join.

Try Exercise 22 now.

EXERCISE 22

You will need the help of a member of your family. Pick a TV programme that you usually watch – perhaps a half-hour soap opera. Place earplugs in both your ears, and ask your helper to follow the programme with you. You will be relying on visual clues in behaviour and facial expressions. See if you can follow the programme without sound. Relate the story back to your helper, and check whether you reflected the story accurately.

Identify the parts of the story you were inaccurate about, and write down why you think you picked out the wrong cues, or why you think you arrived at the conclusion you did.

DISORDER OF SMELL AND TASTE

We use our senses of smell and taste so often that their loss can lead to many difficulties in communication. Lack of smell and taste are often associated. Try to imagine your favourite food with no smell or taste, the hairdresser's without the scent of shampoos or a warm garden after rain but with no fragrance. Smells and taste help us to be nostalgic, to reflect and reminisce.

Try Exercise 23 to help you appreciate this.

Perhaps your client does not make the responses you would expect, such as remarking on the taste of some food or drink. Perhaps he ignores potential hazards, like a gas ring turned on but unlit, or a pan of burning food.

The client may need to have this difficulty investigated. You may already know what could be the cause of such problems, for example, the client has had a head injury which damaged the cranial nerves.

EXERCISE 23

Write down a list of the smells you always associate with religious or other festivals.

After doing this, try to imagine the same scenes or objects without the smells. Would the pictures you imagine be enough for you?

A disorder of smell and taste which is organic, that is, caused by damage to the cranial nerves, should not be confused with some psychiatric disorders. Some psychotic people believe others are trying to gas them or harm them with toxic fumes and some will complain of a taste of poisonous material in their food.

DIFFICULTIES WITH VERBAL SKILLS

When we meet a client we immediately make assumptions about verbal skills from what we see. For example, if our client is 18 months old we will not expect to have a dialogue with him about whom he thinks are our allies in Europe. He will not have the knowledge, words or intellectual ability to express this. However, a man of 43 years with the IQ (measured intelligence) of a two- or three-year-old would have similar difficulties. Both age and intelligence affect the way a client communicates verbally.

The client will also need the physical means to communicate. He will need a voice and the equipment to express the messages from his brain in words. If the brain does not function correctly, as in some of the dementing illnesses, the words may not make sense.

CLIENTS RECOVERING FROM A STROKE

The client who has had a stroke (Cerebro-Vascular Accident) may not be able to speak because his nervous system has been damaged. He may also have lost the function of a limb or a sensation. If the client cannot speak and is also unable to use a dominant hand (the hand he uses to write), his distress in communicating is increased. He will be unable to write down his needs and anticipating them will require all your skills. His repeated attempts to make himself understood will produce misery and frustration. However, if partial speech is present on return to consciousness then speech is likely to improve. Knowing this can provide some comfort for the client.

A client who has had a stroke may be more emotional than normal, due to changes in his body as well as through frustration and distress. After a stroke, a client may have difficulty communicating with himself or with the environment. Sensory input from others is helpful here and having familiar articles nearby, such as a clock or watch or family photograph, can act as a stimulus.

Impulsive behaviour or poor judgement may put the client at risk. For example, if he is unable to judge space he may put down a cup of hot coffee before reaching the bedside table.

If a client has had surgical removal of the voice box he may be taught to speak in other ways. This may involve swallowing air and using the windpipe, which makes the voice sound very hoarse. Some of these clients have a speech aid, such as an electrical artificial larynx.

Many hospitals and residential homes use pictures for the client to point at to indicate basic needs. These may involve needs such as food, water and warmth. The ability to communicate these essentials helps to relieve the client's anxiety.

CONFUSED CLIENTS

Dementia

There are many causes of confusion but the one producing particularly challenging problems for care staff is **dementia**. This was often referred to as 'senile dementia' but can begin earlier than retirement age.

Dementia begins with some mild mental impairment, such as forgetfulness or lack of spontaneity, and progresses through to confusion, agitation, restlessness, aggression and incontinence. The most common type of pre-senile dementia is called **Alzheimer's disease** and it can begin as early as 40 years old.

The care of clients with confusion associated with dementia, and the communication skills needed in this area of work, provide a major challenge for the care worker.

Relatives of these clients also need lots of care and support, and recognition of the tremendous effort they are making. The relatives' resources will be stretched to the limit and it is important that we not only recognise this but also communicate our recognition to the relatives. They often feel alone and that their investment in the care is unrecognised or devalued.

Some of the symptoms of organic dementia are:
- impaired judgement
- little or no initiative
- memory loss (particularly for recent events)
- confusion
- irritability
- lack of personal care
- incontinence
- needing constant supervision.

Where do you begin to communicate usefully and meaningfully with a client who has organic dementia? Rather than considering what improves good communication think about what prevents it. Good communication with these clients can often begin with providing the right environment.

KEY POINT
Confused clients
how increased
disorientation as
evening approaches
and during the night
hours.

On page 33 we looked at the effects of sensory overload and sensory deprivation. If we take into account these two areas in our care of the client we can start to provide the right conditions for good communication.

Now do Exercise 24, using the box below.

EXERCISE 24

Pick one of the aspects shown in the box which describe the various kinds of overload and deprivation – sensory, movement, surroundings, communication, activity and social/cultural.

Write a short essay, or jot down some notes, describing one aspect of your life, for example your social life, or the road where you live, in each of these ways. This may include something you feel is dull and boring, or too quiet. On the other hand it may be that too much is happening and noises and intrusions prevent you from thinking clearly.

When you have finished, analyse how a client might cope with these situations when he is impaired by organic dementia.

OVERLOAD AND DEPRIVATION AFFECTING COMMUNICATION

SENSORY

Overload	**Deprivation**
Hearing: Noise. Chatter. Bangs.	*Hearing:* Silence. Lack of clarity in speech.
Sight: Bright lights. Flashing lights. Constant lights.	*Sight:* Poor eyesight. Obscured vision. Vision affected by medication.
Taste: Forced food. Forced medicines.	*Taste:* Lack of taste/smell due to organic illness. Fluids only, no time to eat before food is removed.
Touch: Rough handling. Pain. Excessive handling.	*Touch:* No physical contact. Numbness. Oversedated.

MOVEMENT

Overload	**Deprivation**
Restrained	Exhaustion. Immobile.

SURROUNDINGS

Overload	**Deprivation**
Too many visitors. Noisy. Small space. Changing rooms. Lots of different care staff.	No visitors. Large, unfilled space. Bare rooms/walls. Little stimulus.

COMMUNICATION

Overload	**Deprivation**
Jargon. Different language. Incomprehensible explanations. Unfamiliar accents.	Aloofness. Suppression of feelings.

ACTIVITY

Overload	**Deprivation**
Endless tests. Examinations. Frequent procedures to go through. Cannot understand the meaning of them.	Confined to bed. Nothing happening. No meaningful activity. Endless television watching.

SOCIAL/CULTURAL

Overload	**Deprivation**
Family demands. Telling you what to do. Lack of control over one's life. Professional demands. Telling you how to get it right.	Withdrawal of family/friends. Socially isolated. Culture not familiar. Nothing to interest you.

There are other ways in which we can improve our communication with confused clients:

- Simplify new information.
- Give written instructions for diets, medication, and treatment: this is essential.
- Do not be rigid – adapt schedules, treatments and care to the client's own existing patterns.
- If possible, teach in the client's own environment with his own materials.
- Use all the senses you can to assist with learning. For example, with new medication look, touch, taste and feel it.
- Visual clues help. For example, picture charts.
- Use the client's knowledge and old learning patterns to deal with new situations.
- Try to evoke responses rather than demand or request them.

Holism and dementia

We can review what we have said about confusion and organic dementia by using the model of the five holistic dimensions of the person, which we discussed on page 19.

Physical dimension – Inability to care for himself, resulting in illness or injury.

Emotional dimension – Easily distressed; mood swings; uninhibited feelings; inappropriate expressions.

Intellectual dimension – Poor judgement; false perceptions; delusions (false beliefs); memory defects; poor judgement.

Social dimension – Disruptive in family relationships and care staff relationships.

Spiritual dimension – Lack of understanding about the meaning of life and what is happening to him; lack of contentment; feeling hopeless.

Try Exercise 25 before going on to the section dealing with difficult feelings.

EXERCISE 25

Look up the word 'judgement' in a dictionary.

Describe how a lack of judgement could cause communication problems.

DIFFICULT FEELINGS

Difficult feelings are not easy, either for the client to handle or the care worker to tolerate. Some feelings bring out the best in us, others bring out the worst. You have to cope with these two extremes of feeling, and as the giver of care you may come up against your own helplessness.

Some feelings the client has will make him feel helpless and dependent on you; you may feel more comfortable in this situation because you are needed and feel powerful. On the other hand, you may feel oppressed by his dependence on you and feel a sense of failure because the client is not more self-sufficient. Many areas of communication are involved in our responses to these different feelings.

ANGER

The word 'anger' describes a wealth of feeling including displeasure, hostility, aggression, fury, frustration and rage. See Exercise 26.

EXERCISE 26

Take a large piece of paper.

Write '**irritated**' at the top, and '**rage**' at the bottom. In between these two words write other words that describe varying degrees of anger. Find someone else to help with this exercise and compare where each of you have put identical words on the scale. For example, 'frustration' will be lower down the scale for some than for others.

Different degrees of anger can be frightening. Anger can be destructive and can push people away, leading to a separation. You may have felt consumed by anger yourself if you have watched this happen to others.

Anger can make you impulsive because you see things in a different light. Anger can also be a warning and is difficult to ignore. It can produce insensitivity to other people and to the environment.

Many people are taught as children not to show feelings of anger, but in a care-giving situation anger may be natural and valuable for the client. We can see anger in this way if we distinguish it from violence and rage.

Rage expresses itself through hitting, banging, running, pushing or pounding and is intent on destruction. Anger can be expressed verbally and discharging it can direct the person towards a more creative solution to his difficulties. Everyone becomes angry at some time or other and we need to be able to deal with anger in ourselves as well as in our clients.

Anger may be displaced onto other people or objects. For example, if a worker cannot express his feelings towards his boss he may direct his anger towards his wife. She, having no one to share it with, may shout at her child. The child, in frustration, begins to tear up his books.

How do we cope?

Working with angry and aggressive clients demands a lot from you. Your natural response is to be distressed, angry and feel inadequate. In your childhood, you may have received strong messages to ignore anger by denying it, so you might simply change the subject and talk about something 'nice'.

The care worker who accepts another's anger with calmness and confidence can often help the other person regain control of themselves. If you are continually the object of anger you must be brave enough to ask if you are doing something to provoke this response. Some common reasons for being angry, given by clients, are:

- inconsiderate behaviour

- patronising responses

- inattention

- strong opinions

- separation

- waiting.

You may discover the reason for the anger by using gentle confrontation. On the other hand, you must not believe it is always your fault that people become angry.

Now do Exercise 27.

EXERCISE 27

Make a list of bodily messages that show people are angry.
For example, 'clenching fists', 'gritting teeth'.

The list you made in Exercise 27 of the behaviour that expresses anger is important because we sometimes fail to respond to what we see and therefore do not intervene before things are out of control.

Anger is a natural response to provocation. It can be both destructive and constructive but, if you can respond to anger carefully when you communicate with the client, both of you may learn from it.

DESPAIR

If the client feels despair we must try to give him hope. Hope defends against despair and enables us to tolerate difficult situations because it keeps us motivated. Despair brings about a loss of hope and confidence. The client is enveloped by it and cannot escape. His life seems futile.

What the client wants is beyond his reach; he has no energy to think of solutions or act in any way to help himself. You will encounter a passive individual, immobilised by his despair. He will feel like giving up and sometimes has done so. He has decided there is no sense or reason for living.

Try Exercise 28 before continuing. It will help you to identify ways of describing the various degrees between hope and despair. It will also highlight words you can use with the client, to help him describe how he feels.

EXERCISE 28

Take a large piece of paper. At the top write 'hope' and at the bottom write 'despair'. In between write the feelings that lie along the scale between the two.

Near the 'despair' end of your list will probably be 'helplessness', 'hopelessness', 'apathy', and 'sadness'. These words are often connected with the idea of loss. When the sadness of grief is resolved the client makes the experience part of his life. If his grief is not resolved he continues to feel anger, guilt, helplessness and despair.

How do we communicate?

Relating to a despairing client is difficult and uses up a great deal of energy. You may feel you will become 'contaminated' by the power of the client's feelings and may defend yourself by avoiding them. The client's helplessness can quickly leave you feeling helpless too.

You need to examine your own thoughts about the client's response. If you feel angry, frustrated and judgemental towards the client you must acknowledge it. Establishing trust and acceptance with this client requires patience and the ability to stay with him as he works through all his difficult feelings.

The client will not be able to come up with answers, explanations, or reasons to go on. He may need to sit for long periods in silence or give only negative responses. Sitting in silence with him indicates your continued interest and availability. Your commitment to the relationship is tested and gradually trust emerges. The client may easily become dependent at this stage, something you will eventually need to deal with.

It is not easy to maintain communication in the face of withdrawal. It uses your ability to persevere without being overwhelmed by the client's despair, rather than good verbal skills. Remember, at the end of the day the feelings are *his* and not yours. Your hope for him, and your perseverance, will be powerful in achieving healing.

LONELINESS

Loneliness can be caused by health problems and it can also create them. The nature of your work means you will be confronted with the consequences of loneliness and loneliness will have created problems that require care. It will be difficult to stay with some of the pain of loneliness and you will often be reminded of your own helplessness.

45

Loneliness can be defined as 'the absence of expected relationships'. The client's attitudes and social skills will have a great influence on how he sees the problem, but he will not realise this – he will simply either say he is 'lonely' or he is 'not lonely'.

If the client feels lonely he will feel deprived or feel something is missing because expected relationships are absent. Loneliness seems to be age-related. It is often felt most strongly in adolescence and in old age. It is not directly related to being socially isolated. **Look at Exercise 29.**

EXERCISE 29

Think of a situation you know about, perhaps at work, where someone is surrounded by other people and yet your perception of them is that they are lonely.

Write down why you have arrived at this conclusion, not only from verbal exchanges with this person but also from what you have seen in their behaviour.

Some people adapt to being alone. They turn inwards and find some inner resources. In others, loneliness causes some unpleasant feelings.

The problems caused by loneliness do not necessarily need outside help. Often, the loneliness is temporary and caused by changes in circumstances, such as ending a friendship, starting a new job or a change in marital status. New opportunities and activities can develop from these situations and reduce the feelings of isolation.

How do we help?

Many people feel that nothing can be done to alter the behaviour associated with loneliness. People are often quick to judge, feeling that the lonely must have done something to deserve being isolated, or even resorting to fantasy and suggesting that some abnormal trait has led to the isolation.

See Exercise 30.

EXERCISE 30

Write down your thoughts on the following statement:

'Nothing can be done to alter lonely people's feelings'

As a care worker you will spend a long time listening to the lonely client's pain and his sense of the futility of life. His feelings of hopelessness often prevent any attempt you make to change things. You must believe changes can occur otherwise you will not be able to convince the lonely client that this is possible.

It is important that you give the client a chance to explore the nature and extent of his loneliness. You may worry that this will mean you have to give even more time to the client, and he will become dependent on you. But dependence can be worked through so don't feel uneasy about encouraging the client to talk.

Encourage the client to explore other relationships, test out new social skills or develop an attachment to a pet. Some clients go into minute detail about what went wrong in previous relationships, in an attempt to explain the futility of further efforts. Remind them that 'we are only human and anyone can get it wrong'. However, you need to be sensitive to their worries when encouraging them to try out new social situations.

The people most at risk from loneliness are:

- adolescents
- the elderly
- dying people
- people with chronic illness
- people with socially unacceptable illnesses
- people with body image problems
- those who have lost significant relationships
- those moving to a new geographical area.

Use this list for Exercise 31.

EXERCISE 31

Pick three people from the list and state why they might become lonely.

The nature of your work as a care worker means you will come into contact with many people in these groups. Their social isolation or loneliness will have a profound impact on the kind of care you give. The client himself may allow you to help him find ways to deal with the problem. This is not only good for the client, but it also reduces the distress and helplessness experienced by care workers who are continually being confronted by the difficulties of loneliness.

MISTRUST

How do we develop trust?

Trust and mistrust will always be an important part of your relationship with the client.

Everyone needs to develop the right balance of trust and mistrust. Someone who has no mistrust at all will be at risk. He will be open to abuse if he does not show caution when meeting people. On the other hand, being too cautious or well defended prevents relationships developing and makes other people very anxious. If you are very well defended as a care worker, and give away little or nothing about yourself, you will experience difficulty in communicating with your client.

Trust cannot be established without honesty. To encourage trust you need to be accepting and genuine. For example, you must not offer help on condition that the client is grateful to you.

You must also be emotionally open or accessible. Your openness allows the client to see something of the person behind your role. By allowing this, you trust the client to find you acceptable and your relationship can become more intimate. Trust develops from reliable, consistent exchanges, in which the client feels accepted, understood and valued. Healthy people assume others are basically trustworthy until they find out otherwise.

As you develop skills of good communication you will be able to prevent your clients experiencing feelings of mistrust. You will also be able to help a client re-evaluate his relationship with you, if he began by mistrusting you.

DEPENDENCE

How do we encourage interdependence?

We begin life being dependent and progress towards independence. One anxiety of both the client and the care worker is that each will become dependent on the other.

Some care workers feel enveloped by the client's dependence and feel it is destructive. Most care workers want to maintain the client's independence by respecting his wishes and giving him control over his life.

Some of the tasks you perform will remind the client of his dependence and may cause him to revert to a child-like state. Imagine what it feels like to be fed or washed when you are an adult. In this difficult situation it is important to try to give control back to the client as often as possible.

It is not easy to give some freedom of choice to people who are dependent on you for their most basic needs. If not done sensitively, it can seem patronising.

See Exercise 32.

Linked with the words independent and dependent is another word interdependent. The interdependent person is capable of using both dependence and independence. This is the best way of coping. Interdependence also suggests that dependence is not a totally negative experience but that it involves striking a balance between doing things for yourself and receiving help where it is needed. Try to find ways of communicating this to your client, to put him at ease.

48

> **EXERCISE 32**
>
> **Feeding someone who is unable to feed himself sounds a simple enough task. Imagine an adult needing your help to feed him a three-course lunch.**
>
> Write down how you might give him control, help his self-esteem, and remove his powerful feelings of being childlike and dependent. *For example:*
>
> If he cannot speak how can you ask him to tell you to wait before giving his next mouthful?
>
> How can he indicate he does not like the food or does not want any more? What conversation will help him feel like an adult and not like a child?
>
> What communication skills will be necessary to do this?
>
> **Note:** Remember how you use drinks with your meals.
> We sometimes remove one taste from our mouths with a drink before moving on to other tastes.
> This may be more relevant between courses.

PAIN

How do we respond?

You often have to confront emotional and physical pain in your work. This can be distressing and the effects can build up gradually. Confronting pain day after day can leave you feeling damaged and worn out. Also, it is difficult to find suitable responses to someone else's pain and the result can be a breakdown in communications. Pain is no respecter of persons, it is a universal experience.

The best definition we can find of pain is that it is a personal, private sensation of hurt. If you describe pain in this subjective way it implies that the individual experiencing the pain is the expert on the sensation.

There is a reason for physical pain because it protects us from harm by warning of current or possible tissue damage. For example, acute pain from a twisted ankle will warn you not to bear weight on it until it heals. Acute pain such as this usually resolves once healing takes place.

Chronic pain, on the other hand, can be a hindrance to an individual's health and well-being. Pain may lead to psychological distress as anxiety, anger, depression and loss of control. It can be all consuming, pervading the whole being, and totally preoccupying the client.

The way you as a care worker respond to pain is often used as a measure of

KEY POINT
Chronic pain results in loss of physical function, social function and in loss of a client's positive sense of self.

49

how much you care for the client. If you fail to respond to expressions of pain the client may feel you do not care about him.

You may find it difficult to continually respond to the ongoing, debilitating nature of pain. You may only be able to show empathy if your client's response to his pain is to be angry, withdrawn and resentful. These responses themselves may indicate to you that the client is in pain.

Now do Exercise 33.

EXERCISE 33

Try to remember a time when you were in physical pain, perhaps with toothache.

How did you behave when the pain was at its worst?
Think about any physical activity caused by the pain and about your attitudes and feelings towards others.
Perhaps you paced around, feeling restless and angry.
Make two lists, next to each other, headed '**Feelings**' and '**Behaviour**'. How did you feel and what did you do?

It is important that you respect the client's response to pain even though you may have different attitudes as to what is an appropriate response to pain, determined largely by your background, values, beliefs and previous experience or memories of pain.

REVIEW

This chapter has highlighted some of the special communication difficulties that occur in a care worker's role. You will experience others as well, but those discussed are particularly demanding. Encounters of this nature can bring out the best or worst in us because our own emotional responses are not always welcome and we can be reminded of our own vulnerability.

SUMMARY EXERCISE

Make a list of your best and worst qualities.

---

5 Practical considerations

Professional counsellors use interpersonal skills such as listening, reflecting, restating, ventilating, and non-verbal communication. However, having some knowledge of them, or using them, does not make you a counsellor. This book is not intended to prepare you to be a counsellor and it is important that both you and the client know your limitations. However, there are some other counselling skills you can employ in your role as a care worker.

BUILDING TRUST

Most clients do not need professional counselling or help in sorting out psychological problems. Some will not know what counselling is, or will be suspicious or prejudiced about it, but they will feel comfortable discussing their problems with you because trust and a degree of intimacy have developed between you. You have become a familiar face and maybe even a friend. If you are regularly involved in someone's care you will take an interest in him. You will be challenged to do your best to promote good care. The client develops confidence in you because of the commitment you have shown to him. Trust begins to emerge. This trust allows him to express his views and his feelings. This may happen quickly or develop gradually over a long period. Sometimes you meet someone and immediately feel you would like to know them better – you feel confident with them.

Look at Exercise 34.

EXERCISE 34

Think about someone you have met, with whom you immediately felt at ease.

Write down what happened and what you think allowed this to happen so soon.

Your role as a care worker will constantly test out your ability to establish relationships. The care worker and client are strangers when they first meet. It would be ideal if the client was always the first to express what was on his mind but this will not always happen. As a care worker the responsibility for establishing communication is also yours; you will need to work hard at allowing useful ways of communicating to develop. By being warm and friendly you can create an atmosphere in which the client feels accepted and comfortable. He then feels able to talk or not as he wishes.

ENCOURAGING COMMUNICATION

In Chapter 3 we looked at general conversational skills. It is also helpful to 'tune in' to the individual forms of speech used by your client, for example using words he is familiar with. Using the same words and sounds as the client, to reflect back to him what he has said, will encourage him to continue speaking.

Using a single-word response also allows further expression of feelings. For example, if a client tells you how scared he was about some incident you may repeat this emotive word as question:

'*Scared?*' or '*Really?*' or '*Oh?*' or '*Why?*'.

Single-word responses show you are paying attention but allow the client to do most of the talking.

HOW MUCH SHOULD YOU SAY?

When you discuss problems with the client try not to talk too much or be seen as an expert about everything. As you gather knowledge about other people and how they deal with things, you may quote them. Perhaps you may feel you should use your wide experience to tell the client all about this problem so you say things like:

> '*Well. of course, in my experience ...*' or '*My other clients always found this useful...*'

This can take away some of the uniqueness your client feels in his relationship with you.

LISTENING

If you are not sure what to say to your client, or are worried that what you say will do more harm than good, remember that listening is not harmful. Sharing someone else's problem with him will do him good. If you are listening and not talking you will be doing more good than harm.

Try not to fall into the trap of interpreting too quickly what the client is saying. Further questions may help *him* to interpret what he has said for himself.

WHEN TO STOP PROBING

Another useful counselling skill is knowing when to stop probing for information the client does not want to give. You need listening skills in this situation as well as skills in picking up behaviour which is a sign of anxiety. Trying to force someone to talk could produce hostility.

52

KNOWING YOUR LIMITS

It is important to recognise your own limitations, both personally and in your role as a care worker. At times you will be faced with clients who require more than your skills and training can provide. You will recognise serious mental, physical and emotional conditions through your training and common sense but you may also be confronted with something that you know, from previous knowledge or experience, requires skills you do not have.

Look at Exercise 35.

EXERCISE 35

Look up in a dictionary the definition of 'irresponsible'.

Jot down some ideas on how the term 'irresponsible' might apply to you if you failed to refer on a problem.

There will also be times when, because of the nature of the problem, you will be very uncomfortable with a particular client. This will seriously affect the way you communicate with the client and in most cases, the client will be aware of your distress or discomfort. Some of our feelings are difficult to hide from a client. It may be that *you* have a similar difficulty or unresolved problem within your family, or with a close friend. This unresolved distress may make you feel vulnerable. In this situation you need to recognise your difficulty and refer the client on, without making him feel the problem is distasteful or difficult to tolerate. Recognising the levels at which you work, and the difficulties you need to refer on, is important for another reason. If you are persistently faced with a certain type of difficulty that you are not prepared for then you, and others, need to review your role. It may be that the role is changing, or some deficiency in training is being highlighted. The care worker's role is not static. If you keep a record of your referrals and difficulties it will not be a list of your failures but a list identifying further training needs and also current trends in clients' problems.

OTHER WAYS TO HELP

GIVING ADVICE

Giving advice can be a controversial thing to do. Some claim that it is arrogant to feel so knowledgeable that you advise others how to act. Others think that giving advice is ineffective because it does not offer choices, but indicates a certain course of action that should be taken. If the client is uncomfortable with this lack of choice the result could be failure. You could also argue that being told what to do fosters dependency.

Most people can describe an occasion when the advice they were given was helpful. Advice given by a trusted person, based on knowledge of, for example, law, medicine, the state benefit system, or bringing up children, can be valuable. Some people are wary of giving advice in case it turns out to be wrong; others make suggestions and leave the final decision to the person involved. Sometimes, advice is given with a 'Look, I know best' attitude.

In a crisis, when the client feels very disordered or disorganised, giving specific advice may be helpful. On the other hand, such definite advice would not be appropriate to questions like:

'What job do you think I should do?' or 'Should I get a divorce?'

If the client asks for advice it will probably be welcomed. Advice given when not requested might well irritate and provoke an angry response.

Try Exercise 36.

EXERCISE 36

Can you remember the last time you were given advice you did not ask for? Write down how you felt about it.

If you say 'If I were you I would ...' before giving advice, responsibility is shifted away from the client to the care worker or advisor. This can give the impression that the advisor is projecting his own needs, problems and values into the advice. This keeps the client's needs, problems and values out of the picture. If the client takes this advice and it does not work then it is the advisor's fault.

Perhaps the most important point to remember is that if you feel it is appropriate to give advice then consider carefully *how* you give it.

Try Exercise 37.

EXERCISE 37

Take a large piece of paper and divide it into halves, head the sheet '**Giving advice**'.

The left-hand column should then be headed '**Negative aspects**' and the right hand '**Positive aspects**'.

In view of what we have discussed, list the positive (helpful) and negative (unhelpful) aspects of advice giving.

PROVIDING INFORMATION

Some problems can be resolved by providing facts. Many of the situations you confront will be caused by lack of information.

Providing the client with information increases his ability to solve problems and make decisions. It is a way for you to show you care and a way for you to give practical help. Putting the client in touch with other resources, such as social workers, counsellors and other helping agencies, can also provide suitable information for dealing with a particular problem.

Another way of providing the client with information is to teach him some of the skills you know for dealing with problems. For example, information skills involve instructing, informing and sharing information with another person. You are not trying to put people's lives right but giving them information to use as they wish. Always give information clearly and unambiguously, so that there is no doubt about the meaning. Your manner should be supportive, providing encouragement to the client.

Try applying these ideas in Exercise 38.

EXERCISE 38

Test the ways in which you give out information.
Take three pieces of paper and head them with these three ways of giving information:

'Clearly', 'unambiguously', 'supportively'.

Ask someone to explain a simple task to you, for example, making a cup of tea.

Do they feel this 'clearly', 'unambiguously' and 'supportively'?

Write down how you think they use each way of passing on the information on the appropriate sheet and afterwards discuss it with them.

Now it's your turn to inform them about a simple task and discuss how well you explained it.

If you have to do the exercise alone, think of a complicated request for information which could be made by a client, for example, for financial advice. Write down how you would reply, using the same three qualities.

Try to let your client know about all the available sources of information. Some care organisations give out information in prepared leaflets or use advertisements in the press. Posters, newsletters and broadcasting on TV and radio also supply useful information. (See Figure 5.)

You may not only work with individuals but also with different sized groups. In groups you can use an overhead projector to show written information or play videos to start a group discussion. Many caring and charitable organisations produce informative videos giving details of their services and these can also be used to start a group discussion.

55

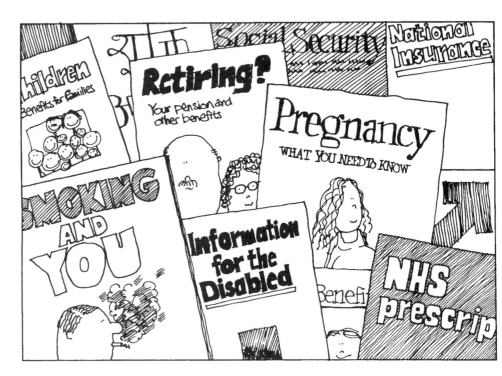

Figure 5
Supplying useful
information

ACTING AS AN ADVOCATE

An advocate was originally someone who pleaded another's case in a court of justice; 'interceding' on behalf of another goes back to Biblical times. Nowadays, care workers are taking on the role of advocates to help clients 'plead their case' and gain access to the services they need.

It is useful to prepare in advance when you are going to speak on someone else's behalf. If you make some notes beforehand you will be ready to deal with departments of busy people who do not have much time to spare. They will appreciate it if you have all the facts 'at your fingertips' and are able to explain your client's needs clearly. Also, being well prepared helps you to speak with confidence and authority because you know which of your client's needs should be dealt with first.

You may need training to help you understand the way various services are run, so that if there are any difficulties you will know how to deal with them and are familiar with the system of appeal. **Now try Exercise 39.**

EXERCISE 39

Think of a client, or some other person, on whose behalf you have had to make a plea to help him gain something that was important or useful to him. It does not need to be a major cause but one which, because of his disability or inability, he was unable to deal with for himself. You need not have been successful. Describe:

What cause you were pursuing.

What arguments you used for this.

The outcome of your plea.

What influenced the outcome.

CONFIDENTIALITY

Most people in caring professions and roles are aware of the need for confidentiality, but we must not assume that the client will know about this, or expect it. Some clients will have heard stories of confidentiality being broken and if they are worried about this, it could prevent good communication taking place between you. However, it is important for you to explain to the client that you represent an agency. Make it clear that, as far as possible, whatever you are told will be held within the agency and perhaps will only have to be shared with your supervisor. Most people will be reassured if you make it clear you will not discuss their confidences with others outside the agency without consulting them first.

Often, family members or others will ask you to breach this confidence. You can usually find a way of avoiding this but sometimes you will have to state clearly that you cannot break any confidences made by the client.

Some people working in a caring capacity have to sign contracts committing them to respecting confidential information. There can be legal penalties for breaking these contracts. If a lawyer, policeman, judge or employer says you must breach a confidence you will need to take advice from someone in a senior position in your organisation.

The case examples used in Exercises 40 and 41 below highlight these difficulties. (Try to complete these Exercises before continuing.)

CASE 1:

For several weeks you have cared for a 68-year-old depressive woman who neglects her physical and emotional needs. Eventually she begins to trust you and, after a great many difficulties, shares some confidences with you. You feel a great sense of achievement, having succeeded where others failed. She tells you she has grown fond of you and looks forward to your visits.

One day she tells you she feels she is becoming profoundly depressed again. She says that, if the downward spiral continues into next week, she will throw herself in the river. Calmly, and with confidence, she tells you it is her decision and her right as a citizen to make the decision for herself.

She asks you to respect her confidence and not to do anything to prevent her from doing this if she so wishes.

EXERCISE 40

List the confidence-breaking dilemmas you encounter in this case (Case 1) and what harm will be done in breaking confidentiality.

What is your decision?

CASE 2:

You are working with a hostile and disruptive 14-year-old boy.

He is difficult to establish any sort of rapport with and resists any attempts to get close to him.

One day he is particularly angry and smashes a window and hits a wall. His hand is swollen and he is in pain. Frustrated by his helplessness and pain, he breaks down and cries.

At this vulnerable moment he reveals years of sexual abuse by a family member.

He immediately regrets this, and asks you to ignore it. He says it was all lies and you will look stupid if you discuss it with anyone.

His ultimate plea is to kneel down before you and beg you not to tell a soul.

EXERCISE 41

Look at Case 2 above. What will you do?

Think about the different skills you would use in communicating with this boy.

DEALING WITH DILEMMAS

No one in a caring capacity should be left to deal with such dilemmas alone. Find out who you should go to for help when you are dealing with difficult situations, or need legal advice.

This is particularly important when dealing with the care of the 14-year-old, sexually abused boy.

Your supervisor will have access to legal advice and, because this client is a minor (a child), will probably advise you to pass this information to the police. It is better if this is done with the consent of the client and every attempt must be made to obtain this.

After your discussion with the elderly, depressed lady you may feel burdened by the information she has given you, particularly if she does commit suicide. Again, your supervisor will have access to expert advice. Some clients expressing such ideas may require compulsory treatment under the Mental Health Act. You would not be expected to have the skills to assess this yourself.

Breakdowns in communication occur if we are under stress or at a loss about what to do. If we avoid talking about stressful issues our communication with the client becomes disjointed. It is hard for useful, healthy communication to take place if we are avoiding difficulties, as most of us know from talking to a relative or friend and trying to avoid mentioning certain issues.

STAYING ALERT

Prolonged exposure to dull or monotonous stimulation can have a marked effect on our communication skills. You may have seen signs in care staff that shows they no longer seem to care and this will also be communicated to clients. How do you know when this is happening and what do you do about it?

DISILLUSIONMENT

In the book 'Caring in Crisis' (1986) ten signs of disillusionment in a care worker are listed. These are shown in the box below.

Look at the list carefully, and think about how this disillusionment will be communicated to the client.

SIGNS OF DISILLUSIONMENT

- Labelling the client, e.g.: 'the stroke patient'
- Feels unappreciated. People are unaware of her difficulties and she does not feel valued.
- Intolerance. Makes sarcastic remarks. Cynical.
- Exhaustion. Always tired. Worries about it.
- Illness and absenteeism. Odd-days 'off sick'. Unexplained illnesses.
- Feels inadequate. Feels lacking in knowledge. Left behind current trends.
- Avoids clients. Finds ways of not talking to clients and avoids their difficulties.
- Unrealistic wishes. Wishes they would not have so many needs or would quickly sort themselves out.
- Over-involved. Has to deal with everything as no one else can get it right.
- Overwhelmed by change. Even small changes produce great amounts of distress.

TRANSFERENCE

"transference"
his occurs when feelings and attitudes, especially those unconsciously retained from childhood, are redirected towards a current relationship

Some of our clients' difficulties, distress and responses can be transferred to us. The fact that the client needs your care may make him despondent about life because he lacks the motivation to deal with his powerful feelings. Some days, communicating with this client will be very hard work. The futility he feels can easily become your feelings too.

If the client identifies you, the care worker, with some difficult person from his own life then transference can occur.

PERSONAL DEVELOPMENT

Some of the predictable nature of your work may produce boredom. This alters your work performance and quality, and your ability to give people attention. Boredom is difficult to hide from a client. Try to remain alert to changes in the quality of your work. Set aside time to stop and look at your own development, and ask yourself some questions, such as:

- What skills of communication have I developed over the past year?

- What are my strengths and weaknesses in this area?

- Has there been a change in my life outside my job that has affected my work?

- What have I done to obtain further education and develop my role?

- What have I done with colleagues and supervisors (or with tutors, if still at college) to evaluate my work usefully, and have I listened to them?

- Is the client group I am working with the right one? Do I need the challenge of a different type of client that develops new skills of communication?

- Are the goals of my clients evaluated often enough? Are my expectations realistic? What do I contribute in my staff group towards the development and support of others?

Although many of your frustrations about communication problems can be due to your clients' difficulties they can also be due to your response to them. **Now try the Summary Exercise.**

SUMMARY EXERCISE

Write a job description for your work, or your previous work, or your role as a student, then list the necessary skills needed to perform it.

Conclusion

The aim of this brief look at interpersonal skills is to help you in your work. You will know by now that there are no right and wrong ways of communicating, but the main aim is to encourage your client to communicate usefully with himself and with you, and to reach his own answers. This allows him to be in control. Our hope is that this book will help you find the resources you need within your clients, yourself and in your training. The exercises will often confirm what you have already learned through your experience of life. We can sometimes make sense of this experience if we put a framework around it.

Most important of all is the care of our clients, and communicating with them presents a tremendous challenge.

SUGGESTED READING

Psychology – A Students Handbook by Michael. W. Eysenck.
Published 2000, Psychology Press, Sussex.

Learning Human Skills (2nd Edition) by Phillip Burnard.
Published 1990, Heinemann, Oxford.

Sage Handbook of Counselling edited by Colin Feltham and Ian Horton.
Published 2006, Sage, London.

Social Psychology (2nd Edition) by Eliot. R. Smith and Diane. M. Mackie.
Published 2000, Psychology Press, Sussex.